OF MOTHERS
& DAUGHTERS

ARAH ILOABUGICHUKWU

Dedicated to the daughters of strong, stressed women.

ACKNOWLEDGMENTS

I first want to acknowledge the people who poured into me as a pupil, three educators for whom my mediocrity would not suffice: Dr. Greco, Ms. Alteri, and Mr. Houser. To Ikenna, the sun I call son, remember that you are infinite. To my siblings, thank you for loving me, considering how much it may have hurt at times. And 'Thank You' could never capture the immense amount of gratitude I hold for you two, Mom & Dad. I owe you both my all. To my exceptional design team, artist Angelina Bambina and the team at The Gallery by MUI, thank you for bringing this book to life. And special thank you to Ogui Agu Eke, Enugu, NGR, the soil that sings the melodies of my foremothers and fathers. I hope that I've made you proud.

CONTENTS

CHAPTER 1

MEAN MOMMY

A JOURNAL ENTRY ON HEALING

I never knew I had mommy issues. In fact, for the better length of my life, I conflated mommy issues with maternal abandonment and abandon her babies, my mother would do no such thing. Now, I would be lying if I said I thought my mother enjoyed being a mother; that hardly appeared to be the case from where I was watching. Motherhood, as she modeled it before me seemed stressful, sleepless, impossible to master. However, I have no doubt she worked hard to succeed.

She gave endlessly of herself, as she believed it to be the obligatory nature of her maternal burden, but doing so with a smile proved partially impossible for her. In other words, my mother was mean, morose, the original nasty-nice, if you will. As much as she loved her daughters, and I don't doubt that she loved us very much, mothering us proved more than she bargained for. I told myself that was her issue, not mine.

Like most mothers where I grew up, my mother was a no-nonsense kind of character, reliable, resilient, responsible, hardly the softest hand in the shed. She was a hard-working woman birthed by a woman who worked even harder than her. Twenty-nine years into that life of labor, she found herself in delivery with me, her flower child.

The baby stage was her favorite; she loved to remind all six of us. That was before we could roll our eyes and catch attitudes out of thin air, you know, the way she taught us. Even our childhood photo albums got thin around puberty, as did the other little perks of being liked, not to be confused with the benefits of being loved. It wasn't an apparent upheaval. On the surface, we were all smiles. The only thing more important than how we felt about each other was what other people thought about us.

Appearances were essential to my mother. Being born a Black woman in western Pennsylvania taught her just how important they were to everyone else. Being a Black woman meant putting on a public performance, and hair and makeup weren't nearly enough to sell the script. Society showed up to see satisfaction, strength, poise, purpose, well-behaved kids, and a happy hunk of a husband. And it was your job to sell the story, to make believers out of unbelievers, whether the role was a reach or not.

Luckily, my mother was an exceptional salesperson. Exceptionally skilled at passing hurt for humor. One of her favorite stories centers around when she swears, I tried to run off with a random white lady at our local children's festival. My rebuttal is that I was four, got lost, and naively assumed the random white woman yanking my arm wasn't doing so to steal me. But she doesn't let the seriousness of the actual story somber her account.

She swears it was a prophetic experience, far more than a painful one, predicting our future relationship's fractured nature. "There I am running around like a fool, and you're busy buddied up with your new family," she reminisces. "Even as a baby, you were running off, trying to do your own thing. Just hardheaded for no reason!" she halfway hollers. There's no denying that in that regard, we are the same.

And while I disagree with my mother's interpretation of my toddler takeoff attempt, I share in her sentiment that our relationship has been a rocky one, noticeably worsening by the end of my eighth-grade year. I attributed our contention to my mother's old-school ways and often hard-handed approach. Other girls were getting mommy-daughter manicures while my mother was outlining the overarching connection between polish and prostitution.

As far as she could tell, it was another case of a young girl getting it wrong. I knew nothing about life, and I wasn't trying to hear anything from anyone that did, at least that's what my mother believed. Our disconnect grew as the Pittsburgh winters gave way to spring. Mother and daughter, we would always be, but neither knew the other as a friend. Nor did we want to.

It wasn't until adulthood that I began to experience just how devastating our strained relationship had been. I had my mother in my life, albeit superficially, but I desired something more in-depth with her and her only, for whatever reason. I often wondered if she longed for the same. It was a matter of familiarity for me. I was echoing my mother's essence in ways I couldn't alone account for. I was coming to terms with the fact that my mother was more a part of me than I'd perhaps anticipated. Without an understanding of the woman whose legacy I reluctantly carried; I was having a hard time building one of my own.

"Damn, I sound just like my mother," I would think silently to myself in the middle of a sentence. Sometimes smiling, other times in tears. Somehow, her influence was still there, even where I longed for it not to be. Life began to reveal the many ways in which I not only mirrored my mother but did so to my detriment, and my inability to understand what kept me tied to traumas women in my family had inherited a million times over. The cycle was repeating through me. And no matter how far forward I flung myself to escape the mold of my mother, I found my feet planted firmly in her footsteps. My only comfort was knowing I was not the only one.

As I turned to friends for advice, and they in turn, turned to me, we found sameness in our sagas. All of us trapped in the pathologies of our parents, desperately trying to discover how we recreated the very environments we worked tirelessly to escape. Was this just the deal with adulthood? Whatever trauma our mothers failed to maneuver fell on us to fix? It sure seemed that way. Our Mother's Day dedications and throwback Thursday photos weren't doing much to mask the fact that there was something about this mother-daughter thing we hadn't quite figured out. And the impact was becoming harder to hide.

The first time my therapist mentioned my suspected mommy issues, I was highly offended. It's not like she wasn't spot-on in her assessment, but I had spent my whole life playing the part. And if she could crack the code that quickly, perhaps everyone else had been playing a part too, turning a blind eye to the obvious – our mother-daughter dysfunction. The truth felt a lot like an attack. More so, my mother's than mine. And despite our past, I felt compelled to protect her, which often meant silencing myself.

As I reluctantly recounted when a boy inappropriately touched me on a third-grade field trip, I paused when it came time to discuss my parents' responses. "Don't get me wrong," I disclaimed, "I love my mother. She took good care of us and would do it again today. We were never hungry, always well dressed, well-behaved, hair always nice and neat. She wasn't a bad mother. I know people whose mothers abused them. This isn't that." I professed proudly.

I had a healthy habit of covering every critique of my mother with a compliment. Where I grew up, talking bad about a Black mother was a big no-no, and bad meant anything absent of applause. Apart from murder, there was little a Black mother could be found guilty of, especially as it pertained to the parenting of her children. And even murder was partially permissible because if a Black mother brought you into this world, it was her right at any time to revoke that gift.

"I can hear how much you admire your mother."

"I do. And I choose to honor her; she's the strongest woman I know."

"Is it possible to honor your mother while being honest about your mother?"

I paused. A piece of me didn't want to answer Ms. Lynn's question. I was confident the right answer was yes, a hard yes, an obvious yes. But honesty was almost too hurtful to be helpful here, or so I told myself.

"Yeah, it is," I replied reluctantly. "I just don't want you to think I'm saying my mom was abusive."

"Well, was she?" Ms. Lynn finally asked flat out.

I didn't respond.

"See, I think of womanhood as one big body of knots," she continued. "A flexible fusion locked together like human handcuffs, each cuff bound to the other, whether directly or indirectly. And what locks those links in place, fuses them, are their shared spaces, you and I call them experiences. As we open and share our experiences, those connections are made. Those connections fortify us to one another, they offer us the comfort of community, but for that to happen, there has got to be a point of entry on either end, right? In other words, someone's gotta open up."

We nodded in agreement towards each other.

"That doesn't mean it's pretty, that doesn't mean it's nice and neat, but life rarely is, and part of the healing process is coming to terms with that fact. Your mother's story is a part of your story too. And you can't hide her story without hiding parts of your own. That doesn't make things easier to be honest about. But I promise you; there's more there than pain if we permit ourselves to look."

I took a deep breath, mentally preparing myself to answer.

"Well, she wasn't happy. That's for sure. She started yelling and hitting me, asking me why I would let that happen. I was so young, none of it registered, none of it made sense. I couldn't understand what I was supposed to have done differently in that situation. Or why she was even upset with me about it, to begin with. I was the one who had been hurt."

"And what about your father?"

"To this day, I don't even think he knew. We kept a lot from him. To be honest, we still do. It's as if my mother was tough enough to handle anything, but my dad was too much an empath to handle the honesty. Hearing that someone assaulted one of his daughters would have ruined him. My mother's concern for our safety was secretly a concern for his psyche, or perhaps the preservation of his ego. America was an ugly reality, especially for little Black girls. I think there was a lot she didn't think he could handle. My mother was almost immune to it."

Ms. Lynn looked up.

"Immune to sexual assault?"

"In a way, yes. It was like my dad couldn't see it. His friends would stop by, and my mother would go into full-on fright mode. 'Everybody, go put on pants, make sure they're not too tight. No sitting on anyone's lap, absolutely no dancing, and make sure you hug your uncles from the side.' Meanwhile, my dad would be yelling at us to greet each uncle, adhere to every request; it was the Igbo way, despite whatever paranoia my mother was masking."

Ms. Lynn's rigorous notetaking continued.

"They lived on opposite ends of the spectrum. I had one parent who didn't see it at all, and another who, that's almost all she saw. But telling us it was everywhere didn't keep us safe. It only added to the anxiety. We were made to feel responsible for the absence of self-control in others and advised to overcompensate for their ineptness with a hyper-vigilance of our own. And when we failed, it was because of our own negligence. The way my mother saw it, if I didn't want Arthur to touch me, I would've made sure he didn't."

"Do you believe that? That, in a way, you invited him to touch you inappropriately?"

"I did at the time. My third-grade brain made it make sense; I had no other choice. It's a lot easier as an adult to disagree with your mom, to think her opinion is a little off brand. But as a kid, it's not so simple," I explained.

"I know now that my mother has some pretty misogynistic views about women and their place in the world, but at the time, I saw things as she staged them. I didn't shout, I didn't yell 'No.' Perhaps my mother had a point. Did Arthur know that I didn't want to be touched? Subconsciously, had I invited the unwanted attention? I didn't know what to make of the situation. I just knew my mother was mortified, mainly by me."

"How did that affect your relationship thereinafter?"

"Well, my mother was distant for a few weeks. That was a very lonely time. I had no one to talk to, and I couldn't tell my sisters what happened. I was way too ashamed."

"Shame and secrecy go hand in hand," Ms. Lynn suggested.

"Yeah. I guess you're right."

"Then let me ask you again, being that you are a mother yourself now, and perhaps that's given you another perspective; why do you think your mother responded to hearing of your assault the way that she did?"

"I think she put a lot of pressure on herself to keep us pure, so to speak. And I guess society does too, so she was really getting it from all sides. For me to be defiled at such a young age made her feel like it was all for nothing. Tainted before the age of ten, why hadn't I fought harder to protect my purity? I think that's how she saw it. I must have wanted it then. And that made her mad. So, she did what she did when she got mad like a lot of moms do."

"She decided to abuse you physically?"

12

I paused.

"I think I know what you want me to say," I stumbled around my words, "I'm just not trying to say it like that."

"Humor me. What is it you think I want you to say?"

"That my mom was abusive."

"Why would I want you to say something like that?"

"I guess because it would be the truth."

"And what's wrong with the truth?"

"Shit... Everything?"

We laughed loudly. *Everything was wrong with it*, I thought to myself. What a horrible thing to say about your mother, and what an awful thing to be true.

"I just don't feel like it's fair. My mom wasn't perfect, but I'm not going to say she mistreated us on purpose; that's abuse. Plus, there was a lot of stuff she didn't think was abusive because it was stuff that happened to her. So, I'm not going to say she didn't try."

"You make some very valid points. Perhaps, I want to introduce you to the possibility that people can be both good and bad. Rarely are people just one or the other. Unless we're talking about Adolf Hitler or somebody polarizing like that; and even Hitler, I believe, could collect a few character witnesses if called to do so. My point is, acknowledging that your mother abused you does not mean she didn't also love and care for you, the whole nine. It's okay to say, 'Yes, my mother loved me,' and 'Yes, my mother could have loved me better.' At least it gives us permission to explore how and break that hidden habit. Give your mother permission to be human, and then you won't need to feel guilty when she is. Because she is."

I had no choice but to consider Ms. Lynn's perspective. I won't lie; I felt cornered by the conversation. We sat in silence for a few seconds. Ms. Lynn cleared her throat to cut the quiet.

"Mind if I make an observation?"

"I don't know if I should agree to anything else today," I joked, trying to tame the fact that I was serious. Ms. Lynn could tell I was serious. We sat in silence a little while longer.

"Do you know how difficult it is to treat an undiagnosed disorder?" she asked me. I didn't. Was I supposed to?

"Ms. Lynn, I know nothing about modern medicine," I admitted. "Is this a trick question?"

"No, it's not," she replied, "and it's not a riddle either. What's the first thing the doctor asks when you go in for an issue?"

"They ask you about your symptoms?"

"Bingo! They ask what's going on with your body to cause you to have concerns. And once we've established that, what kind of information are they looking for next?"

"Medical history."

"Correct, again. You sure you're not a nurse?" We chuckled. "They ask about your medical history to see what's gone on with your body in the past. So now they've got a recent snapshot, plus a picture of your past. What's another important piece of information they gather at the doctor's office? Here's a hint. It may or may not directly have to do with you."

"Your family history?"

"Exactly, Arah. Your family history. Tell us about Mom and Dad, Grandma, and Grandpa, both maternal and paternal, if you can. Tell us about anyone who has ever had to deal with something medically serious. We want to know about them. And not just to keep you occupied in the waiting room under a pile of paperwork, but because the history holds an equally important piece of the picture. We cannot leave our lineages, no matter how far we physically remove ourselves from our families. The influence is in us. It isn't just physical; it's psychological, emotional, spiritual, social. It is the molecular makeup of who we are. And there isn't anyone more centrally synced to our feminine identity than the women who usher us into the earth."

I sighed one long-ass sigh.

"I get it," Ms. Lynn consoled me. "I can't even begin to tell you how many men and women come in here and say they want to find themselves but cannot get on board with having to find other people in the process, particularly their parents. But it would be dishonest of me to sit here with any client of mine and pretend that there is no link between our parents' behavioral patterns and our own. So much of who you see in your fellow adult is based on what they witnessed while children."

"If your mother made an issue about your weight, that interaction likely led to low self-esteem. If your dad

16

dealt with bad news by telling you a bunch of white lies, that interaction likely led to trust issues. Just this year, the *Journal of Marriage and Family* did a study that found that children whose mothers reported higher rates of stress and anxiety had greater instances of both behavioral and emotional problems, and not to mention, earned lower math test scores than their peers.

"We don't have to talk about them, about your mom and your dad, we can just talk about Carlos and any other recent relationships you wanna discuss. We can leave your parents and Pittsburgh in the past. But we can't do anything about their impact. That's there, whether we address it or not."

"Yeah, I understand," I said softly. I was feeling defeated.

"Here's what I recommend, you take the time between now and our next session to decide how evasive you want your evolution to be. We can pluck a couple of pieces of fruit, or we can dig up the whole tree. It's your call. Either route, I'm along for the ride. "

She smiled, and so did I.

"If I recall correctly, at the start of our session, you mentioned you'd recently found a few of your childhood journals?"

"Yeah, my mom mailed me four or five of them. She claims she found them while tidying up the attic, but I know they've been stuffed down in her nightstand for about a decade." I rolled my eyes. Ms. Lynn laughed.

"Would you mind bringing one with you next week? I thought perhaps we could flip open a few pages, examine the mind of a young Arah. That's if you're up for it."

"I get to pick which one, right?"

"No questions asked, it's your life account."

"Okay, I can bring one with me."

"Wonderful. Then, let's end things here for today."

I took Ms. Lynn at her word. And for four years, she helped me wade the treacherous waves of my life, most of them crashing into the current between my mother and me.

The journey taught me to make peace with my mother's role in my dented development and to have understanding for hers. That understanding freed me from my obligation to the appearance of perfection, both on behalf of myself and behalf of my mother. I no longer had use for the shame.

The process taught me empathy for my mother, first as a person, then as a parent, and finally as a disgruntled partner. And I learned to forgive without an appeal for forgiveness, which remains one of the most challenging adult things I've had to do. In learning to forgive my mother for who she was not, I learned to embrace the woman I had become, even if I looked a lot like her.

CHAPTER 2

SECRET GARDEN

A JOURNAL ENTRY ON SECRECY

In my mother's house, there was a secret garden. And deep in that garden, beyond the tomatoes and the bell pepper plants, is where I learned to bury my secrets. It's no secret; my mother's house was a very secretive space where we didn't just learn how to keep secrets but also realized just how powerful a well-placed secret could be.

But far more often than our family secrets were empowering, they were enabling, entrapping even. They were often used to suppress the very things that needed bringing to the surface. And despite feeling conflicted while keeping these family secrets, some by request, others by requirement, I saw the recourse their revelation had and thought, perhaps, these secrets were better kept secret after all.

Eventually, the consequences of our quietness caught up with us. By the time I finished the fifth grade, we were one big fishnet of a family. Sure, we were technically connected, but our decorated disconnect was undeniable. With so much slipping through the gaps, we feared we had fallen too far away from one another to endure the arduous journey back to togetherness. We felt that the truth would break us just as much as it would bind us, so we chose to live in the shadows of our secrets instead.

My mother learned to be a secret keeper from the secret keepers who came before her, and I would take her the lessons she took from them. The first of them is that most people can't handle the truth. Far too often, the truth breaks people or burdens them. My mother made sure I understood this. In my mother's garden, the second lesson I learned was that secrets were better sheltered than shared, even when it hurt to hide them, and it often did. But the most critical component of being a secret keeper was accepting that secrets saved us from shame, and nothing was worse than that.

One of the first secrets I learned to keep was our family's dire financial situation. Occasionally, our gas service would get interrupted. Pittsburgh winters and the weather fluctuations that came with them were almost impossible to budget for. After a week of living by candlelight, I would ride the city bus into downtown Pittsburgh with my mother, hike the half-mile to the payment center, and wait with the other low-income individuals for a chance to ask for a payment arrangement.

One day, our wait was longer than usual, making my arrival at school a lot later than the typical tardy. When a couple of classmates asked what contributed to my tardiness, I told them the truth; that our gas service had been interrupted. Big mistake! It's one thing for your classmates to think you're poor; it's something else altogether to confirm their conspiracies. From that day forward, my classmates made it their mission to remind me just how poor my family was if I ever found the audacity to forget. And when word got back to the teacher that I was the originator of my rumor, she thought it might be time to talk to me about a little thing called discretion. And that she did.

Unbeknownst to me, she shared our shameful little secret with my mother, and that decision turned a would be nothing into a whole lot of something. Upon hearing about my honest overshare, my mother grew furious, although I wouldn't hear about it until hours later. It was impossible to read the room while my mother was at work. Her work voice was a full-on white woman. There was no telling what you were in for once the neutrality of her 9 to 5 faded.

At around 4 p.m. later that day, my mother arrived home from work. In our routine, we all attempted to look busy as she entered the house. Something about seeing her children in a state of relaxation sent my mother up a wall. And so, the sister scramble started as it always did. Feet fluttered from the living room to the kitchen, meals ended, and Nickelodeon turned into the evening news. I can still hear the harsh sound my mother's keys made as she fumbled around at the front door, a sound that has always awakened my anxiety. I'm not saying Matilda's

Trunchbull came torpedoing through our front door every evening, but I am saying, you never knew which Mom you were going to get; one of the burdens of being birthed to a strong and often stressed Black woman.

"Hey, Mom!" we eulogized in unison.

"Hey," she echoed with little emotion. "Where's Dad?"

"He's in the basement," we said in unison.

"Arah," my mother motioned for me.

"Yes, Ma'am?" I replied.

"Head up to your room and wait for me," she said, peering over the pile of mail in her hand.

"Yes, Ma'am."

There was no other response to have, at least not one that she could overhear. The kiddie choir began the orchestral arrangement, against the admonishment of my mother. On any day, we were all just relieved not to be on the receiving end of my mother's wrath. With that in mind, I rarely blamed my sisters for their sordid celebrations.

I shuffled up to my room *per* my mother's rhetorical request. Waiting was always the most challenging part.

You were never sure what you did or when you did it; she lived for that element of sadistic surprise. Her most memorable move, I liked to call the "No-Look Hook," a similar setup to basketball's classic "No-Look Pass." One minute, it was business as usual, the next minute, you were dodging a knuckle for something you did nine hours ago, or worse, something your sister did six Saturdays ago. Right or wrong, justified or otherwise, somebody was catching that nasty "No-Look Hook."

There was no follow-up discussion post-discipline delivery and no debrief to have. There was one rule of law we were all subjected to; that was Dorothy's law, and for whatever the infraction, Dorothy had found me guilty. But what had I done? Probably something like telling lies. I was always lying about something anyway, and could you blame me? My mother may have looked like a little cake-baking church lady by day, but don't get it twisted, Dorothy was no one's damsel, even when in distress.

In an instant, I could hear footsteps approaching the second story landing, making their way directly to the bedroom door. I clenched my fists, battling both fear and frustration. "Fifteen minutes and it's over," I fervently reminded myself. "I can do this," I said as I struggled to convince myself. Just then, the footsteps grew closer to my bedroom door. My heart raced as I tried hurriedly to plan a deflection. Denial was the only tool I could touch at that moment, especially with so little information about the nature of my misconduct. I held my breath, eyes bulged, waiting for my last moments to begin.

Just as quickly as the footsteps stepped my way, they faded into the far end of the second floor. "Hmmm, Mom must be making a bathroom run," I said to myself. Probably much harder to beat ass on a full bladder. The waiting game started, and as I stated earlier, waiting was always the worst part, well, one of them, anyway. I almost allowed myself to believe that she'd forgotten about little ole me and my minor lapse in character. Maybe it was nothing after all, or perhaps someone died. Yeah, that was it. According to the rule of three, we were due a death anyway. As quickly as I found myself free from all wrongdoing, the bedroom door swung open. Standing in the frame was my mother holding her trusted brown leather belt. So much for a mistrial. This sentence was mine whether I wanted it or not.

"Ms. Carter called me at work today," my mother began, slowly closing the door behind her. I tuned in to the details intently, searching for something to contest. "She and I had a nice little talk about you and your nice little talks," my mother continued. "Does any of that ring a bell?" Slowly, my sins began to resurface. The earlier incident she was referring to was when I explained to a couple of classmates why I had arrived at school behind schedule.

"Yes, Ma'am. I remember talking," I muttered.

"Mhmm, and what did you talk about?"

"Our gas being cut off," I whispered.

"Our gas?! What bills do you pay?"

"None," I obliged. At this point, everything I said was being held against me, anyway.

"That's right, none," she snapped. "So, you went to school and said what, exactly, about our gas being cut off?"

"That we had to make an arrangem…"

My response was cut short by the crack of my mother's brown belt. The first lash landed right in my lap, totally catching me by surprise. My mother raised her right arm again, this time lifting the belt above her head. Just as quickly, the belt lashed against my thighs. The sting brought my knees to my chest. She raised her right arm again. This time, she whipped the strap across my crouched body. I winced in pain. She raised her right arm again. And again. And again. And again.

I flipped around the bed in a fit. My body could barely handle the tearing sensation the leather left on my skin. My mother swung continuously, offering advice in between blows. I was too occupied to hear it. As my hands grew hot from the impact of the belt strap and became completely ineffective for blocking purposes, my mind escaped my body for a moment. I could hear the crack of the strap against my legs as I drifted in and out of focus.

The lashing lasted far too long. After exhausting herself, my mother left the room and slammed the door. I curled up under the covers and cried some more. I couldn't wait to turn eighteen and finally be out from under my mother. Sometimes it seemed she couldn't wait either. Like she reveled in every opportunity to free her frustrations.

As I lay there, licking my wounds, I pledged to keep quiet if it killed me. Any and every secret was safe with me. The family business was to be kept under wraps. Under no circumstances did I share with a soul, especially as it pertained to my parents' finances.

And not just their finances in general, but more specifically, their lack thereof. My mother wasn't beating me because I compromised her checking account by sharing a late paid bill with a bunch of fifth graders. She was beating me because she was embarrassed about being impoverished, a condition I was too young and naïve to know was something to be ashamed of. It all changed on that day.

Shortly after the altercation, my father came into my room to console me as he usually did. I sat up to greet him, glad it wasn't my mother motioning for a second round.

"Nne, I'm sorry," he said.

"Please, forgive your mother," he pleaded. I had to hold my breath to keep from cutting my eyes.

"In Nigeria, we don't have this problem," he said playfully. "Everyone is already so poor; it's impossible to hide your poverty from your neighbor."

"In America," he continued, "everything is appearance, appearance. Your neighbor will be just struggling and eating small, small here, small, small there, and you won't even know that he's starving. Everyone hides so well here. It's what they call the American way," he hollered. I couldn't help but crack a smile. My dad had a way of finding the bright side in every sad situation. And this one was particularly grim.

"You know your father doesn't care who calls him poor. Yeah, let them say whatever they want. I know who I am. Don't I know myself after all these years?"

"Yes, sir."

"Eh, heh!" he exclaimed. "What can they say that I don't know already? Let them talk!"

"Yes, sir."

"Eh, heh!" he exclaimed again.

"But your mother has her American way of dealing with things. And then you add the Black American way to that too. I have my way; she has her way. I can't say her way is good or bad, or my own is any better because we come from very different places. You understand?"

"Yes, sir."

"Eh, heh. So, forgive your mom. She is a good lady. I have seen that woman struggle. She is a strong woman. Mhmm." He paused. "Very strong."

"Yes, sir."

"Yes, daughter. Have mercy on your mom. Forgive her. Sorry for that, Biko. I'm very sorry," he said as he hugged me. I hugged him back.

I loved my father, but I hated it when he did that—playing clean-up crew for my mother's madness, guilting us into being the bigger people, forgiving my mother for what he saw as her sin, her temper. Only once did he ever intervene. That's when we all knew things had gotten out of hand. One time my mom was beating my brother for cutting up in school, and as my brothers became young men, my mother opted out of the belt as her preferred physical punishment method. Believing that perhaps, as traditional whipping had become ineffective with them in adolescence, closed fists might do the trick.

ARAH ILOABUGICHUKWU

As the first blows landed, my brother doubled over and grabbed his chest, gasping for air. My mother swung wildly, connecting mainly with his midsection. My brother's body folded in half. At which point, my mother began punching him in his back. "That's enough, Dorothy!" my father finally shouted. "You'll kill him!" He hollered as he hauled ass to the other side of the room. Even he felt that things had gone too far. He was right. They had.

My dad left the room shortly after that, feeling confident that he'd successfully smoothed things over. In his way, he worried about appearances too. He was concerned about the outside world, discovering that his family was fractured. Like most Americans, money was my mother's most pressing concern. She believed that growing up poor put her in a position to pass poverty on to her children. Family, on the other hand, was what framed my father's identity.

Separations were scarce in my father's village of Ogui Agu Eke, a small rural town located in Nigeria's Enugu State. Culturally, it was presumed amongst the Igbo people that divorce just didn't happen. Not only had

32

my father's father abandoned him, but he re-emerged a remarried man. And his new and improved family was no fan of my father. Growing up in a single-parent home left lasting scars on my father, both socially and psychologically. Having traveled across oceans only to form a broken family of his own was a shame my father couldn't carry.

Like my mother feared passing poverty, my father believed that growing up in a dysfunctional family put him in a position to unintentionally lead his children to relationship ruin. So, he vowed to break his father's cycle by forming an unbreakable bond with the mother of his children. For him, peace meant passivity. He believed it to be a conflict that corroded his parents' relationship, so he armed himself with agreeability, whether my mother was right or wrong.

I learned a valuable lesson about secrets that day, even more about the mothers who keep them. It takes more strength to overcome our obstacles than it does to hide what we fear we can't handle. When trauma entraps us, which both family and financial dysfunction are, it can feel mentally and physically overwhelming.

Poverty had exhausted my mother. The compounded concern of day-to-day debt mixed with Black people's orchestrated occupational oppression in Pittsburgh made my mother's situation appear inescapable. She struggled to cope with an adulthood she found fundamentally unfulfilling. Adding the stress of offspring to the situation only intensified the irritation. We were a constant reminder to my mother of the limits on her life; financially, physically, and otherwise.

Maternal instincts are a sticky subject. In reality, "Mother" is just another job title, albeit an important one. So, we're dealing with the individual's specific instincts, and those are often tougher to justify. It was instinctual of my mother to attack when she felt attacked, and by sharing her secret with kids in the class, I had waged war in her eyes.

Her defensiveness was a derivative of the tough childhood she had endured. She felt it was her duty as a mother and a disciplinarian to correct me for my infraction. Still, as an individual, she felt violated and vindicated by her ability to seek vengeance, even if on her child.

My mother didn't have to be proud of poverty, nor did the moment call for a memorandum on her spending habits. But what the moment may have benefitted from was an in-depth discussion on color-coded capitalism and the systemic oppression of women in the workplace, both of which had affected my family far more than I could have imagined.

Had my mother seen value in her story, she would have shared with her daughters the many ways in which these oppressive structures had damaged her, instead of trying to hide the evidence. My mother wasn't wrong in her belief that poverty was a serial setback. It was. And it still is. And contrary to popular patriarchal beliefs, motherhood without resources is hard to handle and even harder to enjoy.

Yes, children are a delight, a blessing, a gift from the universe itself. But raising them, thereby making motherhood a profession, takes more than instincts and feminine energy. It takes utilities, activities, meals, and monitoring: time and effort, organization, patience, and prioritization. None of which come with a womb, despite what men (and women) may think.

The point being our daughters deserve our honest, cold hard, unadulterated truth. In being ashamed of circumstances beyond her control, my mother missed the light in the lesson. She failed to find the teachable moments in her embittered evolution. She couldn't empathize with my innocence while still feeling victimized by repeated violations of her own. She couldn't pull power from places that brought her pain. And so, instead of perseverance and purpose, we learned silent struggle and stoicism, because that is what unhealed hurt yields. It's tough to mature as a mother while nursing the wounds of your womanhood.

CHAPTER 3

YOU BIG BULLY

A JOURNAL ENTRY ON INTIMIDATION

My mother was my first bully. She would clutch her pearls if she heard me say such a thing, but it's true. Sad and true. Now, I never felt she took that position to be malicious, but we are in the home who we are in the world, and my mother was a bully out there too. As a child, I was meticulous about my toys. I lined them up like tiny military soldiers, a bunch of Care Bear figurines carrying out marching orders all over the halls of our house. It's apparent to me now that some undiagnosed sensory processing problems could've caused my compulsion. We knew little about this behavior back then.

I'm sure my mother was curious at first about why my little pony toys lived in a single file in front of her bedroom door, but after a short while, her curiosity bordered on crude. My little tick no longer humored my mother. It embarrassed her.

"What is wrong with this girl?" she would ask aloud. I didn't have an explanation for it either. Besides, I was seven, so there was no well-informed self-diagnosis in sight. I guess I would describe it as having a calming effect over my nerve endings. It made my body feel safe and satisfied. Suddenly, everything was under control; everything was in its appropriate place. Despite my mother's disdain, it was an itch I couldn't keep from scratching.

Many mothers are their daughters' first bullies. Most mothers would disagree with that finding for apparent reasons. In our minds, when we think about bullying, we picture the playground punisher, the lunch money-taking tormenter with an uncontrollable temper. How could anyone accuse a mother of bullying her beloved child, the very child she would break her back for? The answer is simple. For starters, the ability to give birth doesn't dictate our moral methods. Mothers are not above accusations of any sort simply because they've given birth. If our children experience us in a way that we disagree with, we don't get to disagree with their experience. We must understand that it is theirs to have. We don't get to decide that words don't apply to us simply because we don't like their definitions. If the shoe fits, we must consider that it just might be our size.

But who is a bully, if not for your friendly neighborhood playground punk? A bully is anyone who bullies. And what exactly is bullying, you ask? We define bullying as any ongoing effort to inflict habitual harm, coercion, or intimidation on anyone perceived as vulnerable. Our bosses can be bullies; our baby brothers can be bullies. Anyone is capable of being a bully, including mothers and daughters like you and me.

Bullying consists of three key elements: the abuse of power within a relationship, the repetition of the abuse, and the ongoing occurrence of harmful behaviors. This can look like criticism of one's physical appearance within the mother-daughter relationship, especially regarding weight, features, and complexion. Or it can look like public and private accusations that attack morale or character. Mothers do this by accusing their daughters of engaging in sexual activity or engaging in promiscuity without just cause or genuine concern for anything other than the preservation of their presumed purity.

Bullying can also look like the use of physical intimidation, using aggression or excessive violence to address unwanted behaviors and disobedience in our children. It can also look like social intimidation or forcing a child to engage in unwanted social situations. It can even look like dismissing or demeaning a child based on their interests, differences, or sexual identity. All the while, denying the damaging impact these ongoing interactions can have. We call that textbook bullying.

Most bullies learn to be bullies by studying the bully who bullied them. I'd even be willing to go out on a limb and say they all do. Research says most bullies learn these brutish behaviors in the comfort of their humble homes, gaining an unhealthy head start before they ever converge on a classroom. Home is where lessons are taught; school is where the curriculum is tested. Children who learn fear, aggression, and intimidation in the house will use these familiar tools to exert what feels like control in the outside world.

One of the first things we learn from our mothers is how and what to think about ourselves. If Mom affirms who we are and teaches us that our differences don't define us, we learn self-confidence. But if Mom criticizes and condemns us, we internalize self-doubt and shame. Our mothers can be our biggest fans or our biggest defamers. And in most instances, the position they occupy is often predicated on what they believe about themselves. My mother was critical of me because she was critical of herself. And she was critical of herself because she had a mother who criticized her. It was just that simple. Our relationship wasn't a one-off situation. The pain in our family tree hadn't missed a branch, nor had it spared the new fruit. Our story was a remake of the one told before it, and we were closely following the script.

See, my mother comes from a family of fighters. Birthdays, holidays, funerals, barbecues, no occasion was too treasured to throw hands, and by hands, I mean fists. It was a favorite family pastime. You could count on my drunk uncles to flip a table and turn up anywhere we fired up a grill. As a child, I blamed it on the alcohol, but I know now more than anything that it was poor problem-solving. It sounds simple, but trust me, there's a lot there.

Problem-solving is a scientific process, a skill set. In infancy, our tools are limited but not lacking. Babies will cry to bring attention to a need. A baby cries to communicate hunger to its mother, presenting the problem for a solution. The mother responds by retrieving a freshly prepared bottle, modeling an appropriate solution for the baby. When you're hungry, the proper response is to eat. The mother assists by holding the bottle. The baby eats, and the problem-solving process is reinforced appropriately.

This is an example of functional problem-solving for that developmental stage. As we age and acquire additional abilities, like exploring our surroundings without support, we may adjust that strategy. Let's say the child is presented with the same problem; only now, the child is four. They may be motivated to apply the few skills they have to exercise autonomy and solve the problem independently. This, too, is part of the problem-solving process.

The child might climb on top of the counter to retrieve something to eat. He or she might eat something inedible, like the food of a family pet. It is natural for children to explore their options in this manner; after all, problem-solving takes practice, making things frustrating for parents. But ideally, an adult would intervene and model the appropriate problem-solving approach in this situation. And as the child continues to age and faces maturing matters, the parent participates in the problem-solving process, continuing to model and mentor the child along the learning curve, and equipping them with the tools to eventually tackle problems on its own.

We must learn to functionally resolve conflicts during childhood, because we carry these problem-solving skills, when we have them, into our adulthood. It's how we resolve workplace problems peacefully, address issues in our adult friendships, and repair relationships with estranged family members. There isn't a day that goes by that we don't encounter conflict: a flat tire, dispute with a neighbor, or missed flight at the airport. These are commonly occurring everyday problems, which require various skills to solve.

Problem-solving is supposed to be taught, but that isn't always the case. Judging by the reputation my maternal relatives earned around our way, I can confidently say they missed a few lessons. If you've ever seen smudged sneakers turn into a fistfight or a game of spades lead to a shoving match, you know what it looks like when adults lack conflict resolution readiness. I came from that kind of kin.

Our family's methods never matured. No one had any problem-solving processes to pass on. My mother and her seven siblings grew up in a home where they dealt with problems impatiently. My maternal grandmother had a fiery temper, much like the red-headed woman who birthed her. And my maternal grandfather, a lifelong law enforcement officer, had a narcissistic way of adding fuel to the fire. Together, they created a picture-perfect problem.

From them, my mother learned to fight fire with fire and to choose her battles boldly. Their version of conflict resolution looked a lot like chaos, flying saucepans, and

44

pierced voices. Neither of them knew when to say when, if that line existed, to begin with. Imagine toddlers throwing tantrums but with autonomy, with access, and with authority. Now give that spectacle an impressionable audience. The model is bound to leave its mark over time.

My mother held tightly to those tools, confronting conflicts the best way she knew how, with her hands. Unfortunately for me, I wasn't the wrestling type. A hint of hostility was all it took for me to haul ass the other way. My mother saw my sensitivity as a sign of weakness. She saw room to sharpen my skill set. And what better way to learn than by getting your hands dirty.

There was a family that lived up the road from our first family home. A young girl my age lived there along with her older sister, brother, and mother. Her name was Renita. We played together occasionally. Once upon a time, my mother was a secretary at the high school Renita's mother attended. The familiarity made her feel somewhat comfortable with us being buddies.

One weekend, Renita brought a friend to my house to play. Her name was Lanise. Relegated to the backyard, we began a game of hide-and-go-seek. Right away, Renita volunteered to be "it."

"Y'all better not be here when I open my eyes," she pledged playfully. As she tucked herself underneath the crab apple tree folded over our fence, Lanise and I scrambled about. "19, 18, 17," she counted down. Short on options, Lanise and I burrowed ourselves behind the detached shed on the side of our house. "7, 6, 5, 4," the countdown crept down. "She won't find us back here," I whispered to Lanise. Together we waited anxiously.

"Ready or not, here I come. All around base, it is," Renita declared. This meant the search was on. The sound of the grass crashing beneath Renita's feet moved further and further into the distance. "Okay, I think she's gone now," I said, peeking around the plastic shed at home base. "You wanna run first or you want me to go?" I asked Lanise, with my eyes locked on the journey just ahead. "Do not talk to me," she said in a sobering tone. "You are not my friend."

"What?!" I asked, perplexed, turning back to see if she was serious. She lifted her foot and smashed it into my chest, forcing me flat on my back. "I said you're not my friend, so don't talk to me again or imma sock you," she said, standing up over me before sprinting off towards the home base. I sat there stunned for a minute, more embarrassed than anything. I was mad, but what was I going to do? For as much as I came from a family of fighters, no one had taught me how to fight.

Little did I know, my mother saw the whole thing go down. With her face pressed flat against our second-story window, she silently witnessed the entire assault. Later that evening, I faced a litany of questions. Why hadn't I stood up for myself? Was I afraid of Lanise? Did I want people to pick on me for the rest of my life? I didn't think it was that big of a deal. Besides, plenty of people had been pushed on the playground. I knew a few of them personally.

Physical aggression was already a common occurrence among kids in my neighborhood. People would hit you if they liked you, people hit you if they hated you. Hell, sometimes you got hit just for the hell of it. Like most of the adults around me, my mother had little empathy for the exchange, having experienced it herself. "If anybody hits you, you better hit them back." My mother ordered us often." And don't let me find out you're starting fights at school or getting your behind whooped, or you can come home and fight me when you finish."

All my mother's advice did was give me unbearable anxiety. I was so horrified at the thought of having to square up against her that I was willing to walk away from just about any altercation, justified or otherwise. My fear of confrontation made me an even bigger target for it. My mother called it my karma.

Nothing a thicker skin couldn't correct. She thought a little supervised sparing might help boost my self-esteem. "It's a matter of survival," my mother explained. "If somebody's beating on you all bad, it's only instinct to try to defend yourself. You do whatever you have to do to get them off you. Bite 'em. Kick 'em. I don't care what you do, but don't you lay there and get your behind beat. That's what punks do."

"That's right!" my next-door neighbor echoed from her front porch. I failed to mention that this tongue-lashing took place publicly. My mother didn't mind the moral support. She wanted me to know that running from my problems wouldn't work in the long run. At some point, I would have to face my fears. And she was right. Now, how my mother planned to help me overcome that obstacle was a little unorthodox.

Later that month, Renita stopped by to help me break in my new Skip-It toy. Unexpectedly, she brought Lanise along with her. I never told Renita about our little run-in, so I wasn't expecting her to referee our impending rumble. We took the Skip-It to the front of the house, lacing our sneakers while we sorted out who would go first. "Arah can go first cause it's her toy," Renita explained to the two of us. "Then I'll go cause I'm the oldest. Then Lanise, you go last cause you're new to the group." She grabbed the Skip-It and handed it to me. "You get two turns," she said sternly. Renita had a harsh delivery, but her heart was in the right place.

I slipped my foot inside the open loop at the end of the "Skip It." As instructed, I took my turn first, hopping and skipping in syncopation, spinning the bulb around several times with one leg, and jumping over it with the other. Renita and Lanise looked on. "How much longer does she have?" Lanise asked. "Until she messes up," Renita replied. The pair went on observing for a while longer. "Man, she taking too long," Lanise lamented. "Well, it is her toy," Renita replied. Just then, Lanise stepped her left foot forward, bumping the rotating bulb mid-rotation.

"Hey!" I yelled out.

"You get one more turn," Lanise said smugly.

"That's not fair; you messed me up!"

"No, I did not!"

"Yes, you did!"

"Sorry. I didn't see it, Arah," Renita said.

"Man, whatever!" I lamented. Now I was upset. I could hear the screen door screech close behind my head. My mother had made an appearance and was now watching the drama unfold from the doorway.

I grabbed the bulb and gave it a toss around my leg, remixing the rhythm from my initial attempt. My eyes were fixed on Lanise's feet. If she thought she was about to cut my second turn short, she had another thing coming. I was in the swing of things. The bulb cracked the concrete with each rotation, slipping narrowly underneath my shoe. Lanise lifted her left foot and tapped the bulb as it came around the right side of my body. Right in front of my face and everyone else's too.

"Oops," she said sarcastically.

"Renita, it's your turn now."

"No, it's not!" I said, kicking the contraption off my foot. "You messed me up again!"

"No, I did not."

"Yes, you did!"

"Prove it!"

"I don't have to prove it. I saw you do it!"

"You ain't see me do a damn thing!" she screamed, shoving me into the empty trash can upside down on the curb. My back smacked into the can, causing it to topple over. The steel screamed as it scraped the sidewalk. I was peeved. I couldn't believe she hit me again and in front of all these people.

"You better push her back too!" my mother demanded from in front of the screen door.

"You hit me, and we just gonna be fighting," Lanise warned.

"That's okay!" my mother yelled back at her. Slowly, I got up from the ground, my hands covered in dirt and particles. I stood there for a while, wiping my pants' pockets. I needed time to map out my next move despite my mother's instruction.

"Hit her back, Arah," my mother demanded again.

"You better not hit me," Lanise warned.

"She not gone do nothing, Arah. Hit her back."

"Don't touch me again," I seethed.

"Or what?" She chuckled, resting her hands on her hips.

"I know you're not afraid of this little girl, Arah. You better hit her back."

My brain was about to explode. I tried weighing my options but to no avail. The intensity was too high. I couldn't mute the voices around me long enough to ride any train of thought to the station. I had had encounters like this before, but never in front of my mother. I would never have escalated a situation like this on my own; I lacked confidence and courage. But my mother wasn't the walking-away kind. She handled her problems with her hands. And after what she'd witnessed between Lanise and me two weeks ago, she wasn't about to let this go down without a fight. And I mean a literal one.

"I said hit her back, Arah."

I looked up at my mother, who was now halfway out of the house in her house robe. I didn't have a choice. I looked back at Lanise, pressed my lips together, and shoved her as hard as I could. Renita, who had been silent the entire skirmish up to this point, suddenly decided that she'd seen enough. "C'mon Lanise, we're leaving," she said. She reached down to help Lanise up from the ground, but the look in Lanise's eyes said she wasn't trying to hear it.

She jumped to her feet, forgoing Renita's help. She didn't even bother to wipe the dust from her dress; I couldn't help but notice. She surveyed the scene for a moment and reached for a rock about the size of an orange. Before she could successfully retrieve the weapon, my mother forewarned her that there would be consequences. "You hit my child with anything, and you'll be fighting me," she said from the front porch stairs, inching closer to the commotion. Lanise sucked her teeth, standing up straight. "Now if you wanna fight, y'all can fight fair," my mother announced. I must've lost all color in my face. I could not believe what I'd just heard. I didn't want to fight this girl, not her or anyone else. All I wanted was to play Skip-It in peace. Now my mother signed me up for sudden death, and I had no way to escape it. She was going to force me to fight.

Lanise laughed. "She don't even wanna fight me!" she yelled at my mother. She was right. I didn't. "Who said she don't?" my mother asked rhetorically. I wanted so desperately to raise my hand. But Lanise was at least my size. I stood some chance, albeit a small one, of beating her one on one. My mother, on the other hand, was an opponent I knew I couldn't handle. And if fighting her was the punishment for punking out of this, then I guess I was going to have to do what I had to do. Unfortunately, I was going to have to fight.

"So, fight me then!" Lanise yelled in my direction. "Ah! Ah! We don't hit nobody first," my mother made it clear. Without warning, Lanise swung, her fist hitting me in the face. I was dumbfounded. It happened so fast, I stumbled backward a bit, gripping my chin. *Is this how fights happen?* I said to myself in a stupor. *Did I even agree to this?* Just then, she swung again, this time connecting with my eye.

"Hit her back, Arah!" my mother hollered. I thought that might be the best thing to do, but I couldn't connect my body back to my brain. It was like two separate situations taking place at once. I had an out-of-body experience, paralyzed by my fear of both my mother and this fight. Lanise continued to swing. I tucked my chin into my chest and wrapped my arms around my neck. My knees buckled under the weight of her fists flying into my head and back. "Arah, you better hit her back!" my mother demanded again. Easier said than done.

By now, about eight other people had come out to watch the commotion, surprised to see me in the middle of a scuffle but not surprised to see me getting my ass beat. "Is that Arah?" I heard someone ask. "Sure is," my next-door neighbor, Ms. Neil, responded. I could feel whatever little confidence I had escaping from the soles of my feet as I fumbled around in-between blows, trying desperately to stay on my feet. "Why ain't she fighting back?" a kid from up the street asked angrily. His guess was as good as mine.

Just then, Lanise grabbed me by a hand full of hair. Instinctively, I reached up to wrestle with her hands. A

skirmish ensued. My eyes squeezed shut from the sting of
her pulling my hair as hard as she could. I kicked
frantically to free myself. "Don't kick me!" she yelled. I
kicked again. I kept kicking. I kicked as hard and as high
as my legs would lift. Lanise went flying to the concrete.
"Aye, what the fuck!?" she yelled, grabbing her stomach.

"Beat her ass, Arah!" some stranger yelled from the
crowd. I reached for my hair to make sure it was still
there. Embarrassed, I began hand-brushing it back into
the scrunchy she had ripped it from. I could barely
breathe. Lanise climbed back to her feet. "You must want
some more!" my mother added without anybody asking.
I so desperately wanted her to stop talking. I wouldn't
even be in this fight if it weren't for her.

"Lanise, let's go!" Renita rang from the ring
sidelines. "Don't run now, y'all wanted a fight." My
mother fanned the flame. Was she late to the function, or
had she forgotten that I'd just lost? "Let's go," Renita said,
pulling Lanise by the sleeve. "It's time for us to leave,
anyway." To my surprise, the two began to retreat.
Disappearing back up the hill they had hurried down just
an hour ago. I hurried past my mother back inside the

house. The goal was to go to my room and cry until my eighteenth birthday, which was less than a decade away.

"What happened to your hair?" my sister asked as soon as I hit the front door. "She got in a fight," my mother answered before I had the opportunity to explain. My father's fork crashed against his plate. "You say what now?!" he asked, alarmed, rushing from the dining room. "Arah got in a fight," my sister, Patience, reiterated. "Who won?" my brother asked. "Not Arah!" my mother said in disgust. "Damn, baby sis. Why you let that girl beat you up like that?" my brother asked, pushing the loose hair from my face.

I couldn't speak. I was sick to my stomach. I trapped the vomit between my teeth that refused to not creep up my esophagus. I wanted to lie down. I didn't care to answer any of their annoying ass questions. What was the big deal, anyway? We saw fights all the time around here. "Nne," my father addressed me, adoringly, "please, wetin happened?" My father panicked in pidgin.

"She's fine; I was right there the whole time."

"What do you mean right there? You mean you let this happen?"

"Ilo, she can't run from everything her whole life. You mean to tell me kids don't fight back in Nigeria?"

"You're not serious!" my father snapped. "Fight for what? Is it a child's job to be fighting for this and that?"

My father's line of questioning irritated my mother. There was nothing weird about what just happened in her eyes. She felt she had it under control. Organized anarchy, if you will. My grandfather did it to her to toughen her up, and now she'd done it to me. "I said the girl is fine, Ilo." My mother motioned for me to head upstairs. I did so eagerly. I could hear the commotion between my father and mother behind me. None of that mattered. What was done was done.

Later that evening, my mother came to my room, where I'd been licking my wounds most of the day. "If you think that's the last time you're gonna have to fight or defend yourself from someone, I have news for you," she warned. "Ain't no punks in this family. The last thing I better ever see you do is run from a fight," she finished. And she meant that. From that day onward, I made it a point to keep my conflicts quiet. I didn't trust the way my mother handled things. She made matters worse, whether that was intentional or not. If you asked me, my mother's methods were less than useful.

I fought a few more times after that. My mother refereed a few rounds here and there. Each time as awkward as the first. Each time like pulling teeth. Each time motivated by the fear of whatever fight awaited me if I walked away. I had a few bullies in my lifetime, none as intimidating as my mother. My mother never intended to be a bully to her daughters. She didn't delight in exhibiting the toxic traits she was terrorized by during her youth. I don't believe that.

I believe that it's a battle to pass on to your children what you do not possess. My mother was confident in her character. There was nothing virtuous about being a victim. She prided herself on her power and took no nonsense from anyone; she intended the same for us. She felt she did her daughters a disservice by sending them out into the world without the desire to defend themselves. What good was a young girl who refused to fight in her defense, especially in a world where no one else would? She had a point.

CHAPTER 4

I AIN'T SORRY

A JOURNAL ENTRY ON APOLOGIES

I used to steal money from my mother. I know, I know. The horror, right? Obviously, as an adult and as a mother myself, I recognize how big a cardinal sin I was committing and have now for some time, but I feared I had few options back then. See, the importance of maintaining an open and honest line of communication between mother and daughter has little to do with playing posse with your pre-teen. It's about transparency and protection. But here I go jumping ahead.

In middle school, I had a bully. Yes, another one, and her name was Jena; I write about her often. I could fill another book about Jena, with the things I wish I'd said and done, or not said and not done. The thing about bullies is, they get to move on in life, likely forgetting they ever knew you or tortured you at any point in time. You, on the other hand, so much of that trauma seeps into your psyche over time. There's hardly any delineation between your story and theirs. It all started with a bet, not the bullying, the theft; a bet I didn't know I had wagered.

"Your sister said I can pull your hair," Jena called out from across the playground, jogging to catch up with me as the recess bell let out its last ring. "Huh?" I inquired.

"Your sister said I can pull your hair, didn't she, Joyce?"

"Yep, she did," Joyce echoed.

I glared across the playground to see Patience wrapped up in a riveting round of Double Dutch, oblivious to the trouble she had sent my way. I could hear the lunchroom door latch behind me; I was stuck there for the next nineteen minutes. *This is where I die*, I said to myself. *This is where the rubber meets the road.*

My momma said nobody, and I mean nobody was to touch my hair. And the only person I feared more than Jena was Dorothy Jean herself.

ARAH ILOABUGICHUKWU

"Pull my hair for what?" I asked, to buy more time. "Cause me and Joyce made a bet that it's not all your hair. Your sister said it is, but it looks like weave to me. So, you gotta let me pull your hair to see if it's real, or you gotta pay Joyce two dollars."

I stood there, momentarily like a deer in the middle of Manhattan. Shit was about to get real, real fast. I weighed my options; I could let Jena pull my hair, and I knew she would go for a fistful, or I could finally stand up for myself and tell Jena to kick rocks. I reweighed my options, both sounding increasingly, at that moment, like trash. I hated confrontation; there was only one way out of this in my mind. "My mom said not to let anybody touch my hair, sorry." I offered in a panic. I was sorry, alright; sorry that that was the best I could do.

I held my breath and prayed my excuse would buy me some empathy. It didn't. Joyce chimed in again.

"So, you gone give me two dollars then, right?"

"But I didn't make the bet," I retorted. "Why do I have to give you two dollars instead of Jena?"

62

"You don't," Jena interrupted, "if you let me pull your hair. But you won't cause it's fake, just like I said."

"No, it's not!" I shouted.

"Then let her pull it," Joyce chimed in again.

"I can't. My mom said not to let anyone touch my hair." I knew what was coming next: I was paying my way out of this, one way or another. But how?

"Then you owe me two dollars." Joyce shrugged.

"Jena owes you two dollars," I said under my breath. It was my last act of defiance as I braced myself for what was to follow. Now, I can't remember whether Jena was a foot taller than me, or whether I just cowered anytime I was in her presence. She leaned in as her shadow crept up the crucifix adorned doorway that separated us from the cafeteria.

"What you say?" she asked me rhetorically. I got about three syllables out before she shoved me down the three-step stairwell that led to the cafeteria, confirming the line of questioning to have indeed been rhetorical.

"You owe Joyce two dollars, and now you owe me two dollars, and I want my two dollars."

"I do, too," chuckled Joyce.

"Bring me my two dollars tomorrow," Jena huffed as she and Joyce casually trotted back across the playground. My wrist was bruised but no more than my psyche. Where the fuck was I going to get four dollars?

Since as early as I can remember, I've carried stress in my body, never really having a safe space to put it. After these almost daily run-ins with Jena, I would experience chronic migraine headaches; my stomach would cramp up into knots, I would wake up every morning before school, face crusted to the side of a blood-soaked pillowcase. My body was doing everything it could to draw attention to my ongoing dilemma. Why wasn't anyone paying attention?

For a child my age, the stress was becoming too much, which is why bullying is a chapter on its own, might I add. That day I got home from school exhausted, I had a good sixteen hours to figure this out, or I would be on the wrong side of a tribe of timberlands by morning. I ate my usual bowl of oriental flavored ramen soaked in hot sauce and tried to settle in for an episode of *Kids Incorporated,* my regular after school routine. But I could neither eat nor focus. I had to get the four dollars, which in elementary school slang was five dollars, and which in poor kid slang might as well have been one million. I dumped out every change jar in the house. Between the dimes, nickels, and quarters I'd permanently borrowed from my siblings' savings jars, I was just about halfway there. Not good enough.

Ideally, I would have had the confidence to go to my mother about my playground pest. I would've gone to her looking for protection and received just that in an ideal situation, but most real-life situations aren't ideal. My mother raised no punks, but I would be lying if I said a couple of us weren't docile as hell. Honestly, no one prepared us for the realness of the realities we would be experiencing throughout our adolescence, and that realness wasn't always pretty. Coming from a tough neighborhood where fighting and conflict were a source of survival, my mother vowed not to raise her daughters to be like her and her sisters.

But we came from a tough neighborhood, one not that much different from hers, and the other kids were raised like my mother and her sisters, something we were not prepared to deal with. Instead of seeing my mother as an ally at that moment, I saw her as a potential threat. She was far more like Jena in that regard than she was like me. Jena saw violence as a quick means to an end, and my mother hardly disagreed. I was stuck between a rock and a hard place. Going to my mother to express concern, worry, and fear, God forbid! Dorothy Jean didn't raise any punks. Except, she did.

I didn't want to fight Jena, and I didn't want to "fight" my mom as punishment for not wanting to fight Jena, a strange set of options to present to a kid. Just as I didn't have the tools to deescalate a situation with Jena or my mother, they didn't have the temperament to deescalate an issue with a girl like me.

And so, I found myself weighing another sad set of options, I could take half the money to school and accept the rest of the punishment, or I could tell my mom I was dodging a duel and needed two dollars to do it. I quickly shot down both options. Indeed, I told myself, there must be another way. I was going to find two dollars somewhere, and find it I did, in the side pocket of my mother's purse. At one point during the heist, I thought that my heart would pierce through the pocket of my baby blue uniform shirt. I had never been that nervous in my life.

The floor screeched as though each floorboard was reinforced with an amplifier. I held my breath as if that were the solution to hushing the hundred-year-old hardwood. I loosely counted about three dollars and some change before darting from my mother's room without so much as a heel hitting the floor. I barely ate dinner. I was too paranoid. My mother had a way of finding things out, no matter how well you thought you'd hidden them. She credited Jesus Christ himself for that gift.

I figured it was only a matter of time before she discovered my little dealing, and I was right. In the *interim*, the bets continued, as did the intimidation. In the beginning, a shove here or there got the job done, but as the demands became more daunting, and the extractions increasingly dangerous, she gradually upped the ante, and the stakes grew higher.

I was now regularly stealing from my mother to pay Jena and whomever she'd invite to the payout party. For a moment, I thought my mother wouldn't notice a couple of dollars missing here and there. As a bill-paying adult who checks their mobile banking statement at least six times a day, I know better. My mother likely knew right away, although she waited to be sure to confront me. Scorpio woman through and through.

My wide-gazed silence was likely a dead giveaway during her arraignment. The beating that followed was unforgettable. To make matters worse, Jena would later deliver one of her own. Both leaving me depleted, downright despondent.

At that moment, I couldn't see past my victimization to understand how I, too, had become complicit in victimizing another person: just like my mother had done to me.

I never apologized to my mother. I became even more hardened after the experience. I didn't need punishment; I needed protection. Why couldn't anyone see that, especially her? I hyper-focused on my mother's wrongdoing because it allowed me to understate the severity of my own, even in my adolescence. I settled into my victim identity; I swore the situation taught me nothing, except for highlighting who else I could not trust. I was wrong about that too. But what I missed out on was an opportunity to learn the importance of accountability.

Whenever I contributed to my mothers' lack of trust in me, I helped maintain an environment that served neither of us any good. We had our pre-existing issues, but I can honestly say stealing from my mother soured our relationship in a way that previous violations had not.

Before my mother was anyone's mother, she was Pittsburgh-bred Dorothy Jean, the feisty, confident, resilient first-born who took no crap and spoke her mind.

Motherhood hadn't stripped her of her basic human composition. It hadn't hardened her to betrayal or jaded her to emotional adversity. Had it have been a bum off the street who had stolen from my mothers' purse, I know she would have been just as jarred.

My being her daughter didn't lessen the letdown of the situation. It rather worsened it. Somewhere within the role of mother and daughter exists two individuals. Yet, there is an inference implied based solely on our social expectations of those occupying said positions, especially as it pertains to the role of mother, which restricts the individual's realness.

I felt that my mother should've understood my sticky situation, and I still believe that to be true, but I hadn't even considered hers. She was my mother, true, but she was a hard-working woman who gave her all to her family, cried in silence, and always maintained a firm front. She gave too much to have what little she had taken from her, especially to satisfy some playground punk. Theft of any sort is a violation. Theft from someone who exits in perpetual servitude to you, that's emotional violence.

The presence of distrust that occupies the relationship between myself and my mother has haunted me well into my adulthood. Until recently, I was unwilling and unable to see how I, even in my adolescence, had been a contributing factor to that. We both had. How could we not? To this day, I reflect on the complexities that exist within her, and she, the ones that exist within me. But as that reality took shape in my spirit, that I had been complicit in our mutual cynicism, I accepted that the next step had to be acknowledgment. Here would be a great place to ask why.

We can be both wronged and wrong at the same time. As time passes, pushing our trauma out of focus, our perspectives can expand, as can our abilities to revisit these instances without the emotional tremor. And somewhere in that moment of clarity exists the opportunity to consider more than our moment.

There is no healing between two people; actual recovery, the kind that reaches the root of the brokenness and doesn't call for accountability from them both. Healing is about being on the same page, not the right side or even the winning side. In taking ownership of our choices, even as they encompass our childhood choices, we choose to be an accelerant in our healing, not an accomplice.

There is nothing sweet about a sorry, twenty-five years past due. And as attempts to revisit my version of events turned into an emotional tussle, I thought, for a moment, that an apology was too far out of the left field. Over time, I realized it wasn't the apology my mother was rebutting; it was how we arrived at it. I wanted my mother to understand the why, but an unintentional shift in blame accompanied the why.

What I was saying was, "This is why I stole from you." What she was hearing was, "And here's how you made me do it." To move forward in our healing process,

I had to suppress my appetite for empathy at that moment. I needed to approach this discussion from an angle that acknowledged my mother's innocence, and in no way did that absolve her of the many things she was guilty of.

Make no mistake; apologies are powerful. And sometimes we don't know we've been wounded; we just wake up to scars. Therefore, it is essential to know one another as people, just as much as we know our positions' responsibilities. Regardless of age, grade, or social status, people are owed apologies when they are wronged, period! We want to be on the winning side of our mother-daughter relationships, not to be confused with the right side. And to get on the right side of our relationships, we must first acknowledge where we've been wrong.

CHAPTER 5

HEY, GIRL, HEY!

A JOURNAL ENTRY ON SISTERHOOD

My mother's distrust in me taught me to distrust other women. I sharpened that sentiment on my sisters. See, the mother-daughter bond is a young girl's first sample of what sisterhood looks like. If that bond is built on healthy boundaries, the girl learns that sisterhood requires respect. If that bond is built on honesty, the girl sees that sisterhood takes trust. If that bond is built on togetherness, she learns that sisterhood calls for emotional closeness. But when secrecy and suspicion bolster the mother-daughter bond, a young girl learns that leverage is more important than intimacy. When apathy and attitude precede the appearance of partnership, a young girl learns to normalize the idea of opposition amongst women. She cements this stance to her psyche. I learned to distrust women through my mother's demonstration of distrust in me. I sharpened that sentiment on my sisters.

My six sisters and I didn't start as enemies. In our younger years, we were inseparable, particularly Patience and I. Patience was born two years before me. We did everything together, played together, went potty together, baked mud pies together, and ate them together too. Patience was my best friend, and I was hers. When she struggled through her first year of school, I'd be the one sent by her side. I wasn't the least bit excited to be sitting behind a desk at the age of four, tiny legs dangling above a stack of books, but I looked forward to finding my big sister in the hallway. Seeing her put me at ease as I hopped out of lunch lines to hug her. "That's my big sister," I'd tell anybody who would listen. I was proud of Patience; I didn't care who knew.

As we grew older, our differences became more pronounced. Patience was pushy, often urging me into trouble. I was moody, losing interest over the most minute things. Patience was practicing self-preservation before it was even a thing, always eager to put herself first. On the other hand, I was a bit of a pushover and had a hard time saying no. Patience had no problem with that. Still, we remained close friends. Despite our fundamental differences, I adored Patience, my big sister. But middle school brought with it a host of changes, changes that would reconfigure our relationship forever.

I remember the day it happened. They hurried us home from school after Patience had a run-in with the nurse's office. We sat silently for our two-bus bus ride back to the North Side of town. Patience stared out of the window. My mother faced the front of the bus. Had Patience gotten sick in school? I wondered. Why wouldn't anyone tell me what was going on? I hated that my mother treated me like a toddler, too young to be told the truth, too much a kid to be considered. Why wouldn't anyone tell me about what happened to Patience?

Later in life, I learned that situations like these likely led to my debilitating adult anxiety—the recurring stressful situation without any input or explanation. Knowing just enough about the things happening around me to feel physically included, but never enough to feel fully informed. Being left to sit with what little knowledge I had of a situation, and ponder all the many potential outcomes, unable to keep from narrowing in on the negative. I grew sick worrying about Patience, anxious at whatever bad news I had yet to receive. Upon returning to the house, she went straight to our bedroom; I waited for what felt like forever before following her there.

"What happened?" I whispered, pretending to change out of my school clothes. "I don't wanna talk about it." Patience murmured. It devastated me. We told each other everything.

"I won't tell Mom, I promise."

"Leave me alone, Arah!" she snapped.

My little feelings were hurt. I ran back downstairs, still in my uniform. I made my usual bowl of ramen noodles and tried to tune into an episode of *Kidz Incorporated* with Gia, who was two years younger than me. My mom was mum on the situation, unsurprisingly so. She loved a good secret; the juicier the secret, the more satisfying it was to sip on. All I could think about was what happened to me when I started to behave that way, staying secluded in my room for days without food. If some boy hurt Patience, I was going to beat his ass. I wasn't going to let her feel bad about it by herself, not like me.

I joined in singing the theme song with Gia but found myself struggling to get into the show. The situation with Patience had me mentally occupied. I snuck down the basement stairs to where my father prayed and puffed cigarettes before heading off to work.

"Daddy!" I called before slowly creeping down the creaky wooden stairs. My mother hated it when we bothered him before work, but he never seemed to mind. He never made me feel unwelcome.

"Yes, Nne?" he sang. I admired the way his foreign fluency fought to remain a part of our childhood. No matter how acclimated to our American climate he tried to become, Igbo just had a way of keeping him connected to his distant home. And being born into an ethnic group attached to a culture that I couldn't physically touch made my father's refusal that much more meaningful, even if it weren't his intent. No matter how far from Nigeria we were, he never missed an opportunity to remind us that we were the daughters of Ogui Agu Eke. 'Nne' had a meaning that the translation alone couldn't transfer. It meant home.

"Did someone hurt Patience at school?" I asked, seriously concerned. "How come we came home early?"

"Nne, no one hurt Patience. She is just having her monthly cramp," my dad attempted to explain. "Don't worry for her. She will be fine by God's grace." I could tell he had no idea what he was talking about.

Instantly, I felt fear for my sister. I didn't know what all a monthly cycle entailed, but I knew it was nothing fun. My two eldest sisters had horrible cramps. There were days my mother turned up the television to drown out the dreariness of their groans. She swore they were overly dramatic, doing her best to downplay the pain. "You worried about cramps? Wait till you have kids," she would warn. I wasn't looking forward to becoming a woman; look at all the chaos that came with it.

According to the scriptures, being shouted every Sunday by the saints in the pulpit, we could thank Eve for our painful purpose. It was our burden to bear the pain, a curse we carried straight through the gates of the Garden of Eden. Women were hard-headed, my mother warned. And some odd centuries later, we were all paying the price to prove it. Getting your period was a part of the ever-agonizing coming of age for a young girl, a recurring reproductive process during which a young woman sheds her uterine lining in anticipation of egg fertilization. I didn't exactly understand how it happened; I don't believe my mother did either. But I knew that once it happened, there was no going back. And based on what I'd seen, I was fucked.

There was no internet for me to reference—no podcasts produced to educate young girls on the gift of womanhood. Instead, I turned to an Always Pads pamphlet on periods, which my mother brought home from work for us to read. That was her way of talking to her daughters, which, unfortunately, didn't include much discussion. The pamphlet contained a color-coded diagram of the female reproductive system. "What is a Period?" read boldly across the crinkled cover. This looked awful. Just as disgusting as my mom described it. Bleeding every month for any length of time was painful to even think about. And why did it have to hurt? Wasn't the bleeding bad enough? I felt so sorry for Patience. Everything was fine just a few hours ago. Was this happening, and right before Book Fair day?

It wasn't just what was happening to Patience's body that I was worried about; it was what would happen to her personality that scared me even more. I had seen with my own eyes weird things happen when girls got their periods. When my big sister Tola hit puberty, puberty hit back. She and my mom argued about everything. My mom said it was Tola's body that confused her, had her thinking she was grown when she wasn't. She took pleasure in correcting Tola, repeatedly putting her in her place, a child's place. She was no woman, not even close, just a child with a chest.

My mom had no issue reminding her that a fertile womb didn't make her a woman. She spent so much time making sure we understood this; she forgot to teach us what being a woman was really about. Instead, she fixed her focus to our anatomy and invited the world to weigh their opinions.

My mother summed it up simply." Getting your period means you can get pregnant." And in her mind, that made you less of a resource to the family and more of a risk. According to her, plenty of girls got their periods in elementary school, especially the little fast ones, the same ones that were probably pregnant before their eighth-grade graduations. According to my mother, it wasn't uncommon for a young girl to throw her life away chasing after a man. But that wasn't going to be our destiny, not if Dorothy Jean could help it.

I ran to the kitchen to grab a powdered donut for Patience. I figured she might want something sweet, based on what I heard about hormones. I grabbed two pads from my mom's period purse, a tiny tote she designated for her feminine fashions. She had every sized pad and panty liner in that thing, perfect for an emergency occasion, and this was absolutely an emergency. I tiptoed to the room, nudged open the door, and found Patience burrowed beneath her blanket. Before I could call her, she poked her head out from underneath the cover.

"Arah, what do you want?" she objected immediately.

"Just tryna bring you a care package," I said while smiling, opening a paper towel to reveal the dusted donut. "I don't want that," she snapped.

"Okay, well, I brought you some pads in case you need them."

"I don't need those either," she snapped. "Now, can you please leave?!"

"But Daddy told me you got your period in school, and that's why we had to leave early, so I thought you might need some stuff to help you get through it."

I parked at the foot of her bed. "That's not even how it works, Arah," Patience sighed. "Does Mom know you're up here?"

"Yeah," I lied. "Does it hurt down there?"

At that point, Patience ran out of patience, "Arah, get out!" she shouted. Her announcement alarmed my mother, who followed up with her own set of instructions. "Arah, get your behind down here and leave your sister alone!" *What the hell! I was only trying to help.* Puberty was changing Patience already; I could see it happening.

I went to school by myself the next day, which sucked. I was already beginning to hate school, and I had my reasons. Right around the fourth or fifth grade, a separation occurs between kids. The confident ones grow in self-awareness; they may begin to embrace challenges that play to their perceived strengths. With family and friends' support, they engage in activities that affirm, uplift, and offer them a reward for their willingness to take risks. They begin to develop a sense of who they are and who they can be in the world, even if they don't have a long-term plan for achieving that identity. Confidence makes a world of difference in our early adolescent development, almost entirely responsible for how we attack the intricacies of adulthood. More than a lack of tangible goods and a lack of access to means; it is a lack of confidence and low self-esteem that sets a child up for failure. I was well on my way.

This made school particularly painful. The downside of this dynamic amongst kids is that their society doesn't allow that divide to deepen with dignity. As the gap grows, and children become more aware of changes in their peers, some choose to capitalize on the lack of confidence in others, seeing the situation as an opportunity to elevate themselves. Some take advantage of their peers in what is perceived to be a playful way, teasing them about things they know are a struggle, like athleticism or academics. Moreover, some take advantage of peers in a more personal way, using violence and physical pain to punish perceived inadequacies.

I lacked confidence, and my peers were taking notice. Usually, I could hide behind Patience on the playground or sneak outside her classroom door just to sit there and wave like a weirdo. Not today, I was on my own. "Where's your sister," a few of her friends asked as I boarded the school bus. "She's not feeling well," I informed them. "Yeah, she got her period in art class," one of her classmates chimed in. The expressions on her friends' faces changed. "Ooh, she's not sick," one of them consoled me. "It's normal. I got mine too." A few of the other girls at the back of the bus nodded; they had too. "And eventually, you'll get yours," she added. As if that were any consolation.

The day dragged. Hiding out all day was hard. I didn't have the most profound reason; I was just growing into my awkwardness. Patience was a buffer between my classmates and me. Things scared me. Everything, really, especially people and their opinions. I would get so hung up on how to blend in that I stood out like a sore thumb. My jokes were ill-timed, my humor was dry, my demeanor even more dehydrated, and I had the nerve to be shy. Patience helped people not to hate me, albeit for no reason. "That's my little sister, you just got to get to know her," she'd say, prepping people for my off-brand Black girl-ness. Somehow it worked. I didn't care how. I only hoped it wouldn't change, cause Patience sure had. Call it selfish, but I didn't know how much more on my own I'd survive. I needed my big sister and her support. Unfortunately, I wouldn't have either very much longer.

By the time I arrived home from school, I was tired of this menstruation mess. Was I supposed to go to school alone for the next five days? Surely, there was something we could do to speed this up, I assured myself. As I stepped onto our front porch, I committed to figuring this out. I was going to free my sister from puberty, right after the afternoon episode of *Kidz Incorporated*. Before I could drop my book bag at the door, I heard a familiar voice. "Thank you, Mr. Ilo," the voice called from behind the dining room wall. It was LaResha, my sister's best friend from St. Benedictine School. And I hadn't the slightest clue why she was in my house. Rarely were we permitted to have company, and especially on a school night. This was unheard of. *The hell is she doing here?* I said to myself. Had something else happened to Patience? LaResha and I smiled at each other as she passed me in the entryway, heading up the stairs to the third floor where Patience was waiting. I was pissed.

"I thought Patience didn't want to be bothered," I asked my mom, bursting into her bedroom. I caught myself before my dad could; greeting your parents always came first. It was the Igbo way; my father hammered into our heads, no matter how annoying.

"Sorry. Good afternoon, Mom. Good afternoon, Dad."

"Hey," she greeted me back. "Now, what are you asking me?"

"How come LaResha is here? I thought Patience wasn't feeling well."

My mother peered up from the city paper. She could see she was my last resort; I had been everywhere else for answers. No luck. Instead of her usual avoidance, she offered me a partial explanation.

"Patience is dealing with something you're too young to understand right now. And she wanted to be around someone who could understand, so she called LaResha; I said it was okay for her to stop by. Is that alright with you?"

"Why can't you explain it to me?" I asked. "I'm gonna get mine too."

"Why would you want that?" she said, setting down the paper. "Do you see what your sisters go through every month? That's what you're looking forward to?

"I don't have to want it for it to happen to me, Mom."

She sucked her teeth, snatching the paper back up off the table.

"Y'all wanna be grown so bad; you'll see what it's all about."

My mother was no help. To her, puberty was a pain in the ass. And having her daughters enter young adulthood one by one only appeared to compound that pain. It's like she anticipated the problems puberty would bring with it. She wouldn't even consider the possibility of a coming of age that wasn't agonizing for both of us. And her expectations shaped her interactions with all her daughters once we crossed that adolescent threshold.

I snuck upstairs and tucked myself outside our bedroom door. If I wasn't going to be invited into the inner circle, I would sit right outside of it. About five minutes into my eavesdropping efforts, Patience yelled out, "Mom! Can you tell Arah to get away from the door!" I scrambled across the hallway to hide in the next bedroom. "Arah!" my mother yelled. "Get down here and start on these dishes!" I couldn't believe it. Patience never chose her friends over me. What Mom said must have been real. Puberty just made you different.

Patience was a local celebrity at school the next day. Her friends huddled around her to discuss her overnight evolution. Even a few teachers had heard what happened and checked on her to ensure she was doing alright. She still wouldn't talk to me about it. Despite the fanfare it caused, her secrecy screamed shame. After all, periods were plain nasty, that's what we'd been told. A part of her felt seen for the first time, a little more notice than usual. Another part of her bought into the idea that her period pushed her into a separate part of society, an inner circle of sisterhood, one I couldn't understand.

Slowly, Patience and I drifted apart. That separation grew over the summer. Once my older sister, Temi, moved out of our family home, my mother expected Patience to fill that void. That meant managing the kids when my parents were away and preparing meals multiple nights a week. When my mom was away, Patience played the part. Our sisterly secrecy, which wasn't much to begin with, all but drifted away. Patience was an extension of my mother, which meant she became less like a sister to me, and even less like a friend.

When Patience got free time, she spent it all at the park with LaResha. I never knew what they did there, but I would have given anything to join. When Patience pulled away from me, I lost much more than just a closeness with my sister: I lost my link to the outside world. *All this over some dumb ass period*, I said to myself. I could be like LaResha; I was cool enough; I only needed my sister to see.

One Sunday, Patience broke curfew coming in from the park, which was less than two miles away. LaResha invited her over for a movie after their weekend rendezvous. And as it grew late into the evening, Patience fell asleep. LaResha's parents didn't find it urgent enough to wake her. After all, how much harm could she do from her best friend's bedroom floor? Well, they hadn't accounted for my mother's anxiety, which within an hour of Patience's missed curfew, had hit the roof. By the time she spoke with LaResha's mom, it was well past our bedtime. She was livid. We drove recklessly to retrieve Patience; my mother could barely contain her anger. As quickly as the car door closed, my mother lost all control, Punching Patience repeatedly before we could even pull off from in front of LaResha's flat. Blood poured from the fresh cut on her top lip.

Watching anyone you care about being beaten without an ability to defend them physically does something to you. It makes you feel powerless and pathetic. That's how I felt. I wanted to help my sister and tell my mother I thought she was overreacting, but look who we were up against. Did I want to divert the attention to me? Patience cried the entire way home. "You think you grown, don't you?" my mother demanded to know. Patience knew better than to answer.

She didn't ask about the park for weeks, which appeared to be a good idea. Instead, she turned up the charm and seemed to be working her way back into my mother's good graces, caring for my younger siblings, and straightening up every evening without being asked. She was gearing up for something; I could sense it.

That following Saturday, she finally asked if she could accompany LaResha to the park for a birthday party. My mother made her way through the standard line of questioning: who would be there, who was the party for, what time would the party end, and how did she plan to get there; cause my mother was no chauffeur. After pleading her case, Patience got the okay to attend, but on one condition: she took me with her.

I could see the devastation in her face. She hadn't planned for this part of the negotiation. But if she randomly retracted her request, she knew my mother would think something was up. And whenever Dorothy got suspicious, pregnancy tests appeared. Needless to say, Patience agreed to the terms. I couldn't wait. For the first time, I would get to go to the park with Patience and LaResha. I pictured a theme park of possibilities in my head; I was confident I could capitalize on the opportunity. *Patience was going to wish she'd invited me sooner*, I said to myself. And I was wrong often.

Now, LaResha's mom didn't mind playing chauffeur and offered to drop us off at the party. There was plenty of quiet conversation between LaResha and my sister; I could smell the irritation in the air and knew they didn't want me there. I didn't care. LaResha's mom pulled into what appeared to be an empty park pavilion.

"What time do you want me to pick you guys up?" She sounded unalarmed.

"We should be ready around five," LaResha responded. I climbed out of the car, attempting to look as unalarmed as everyone else. I sat quietly on an empty swing and waited as LaResha and Patience discussed back and forth for a little while.

A black Ford Taurus pulled up to the pavilion about twenty minutes into our wait. Two young men exited on each side. *They must be here for the party*, I told myself. I was still struggling to understand why it was starting so

92

late. These people must be Nigerian, I joked. Because boy, did we know a lot about being late. It turns out the party people were right on time. And not only were they right on time, they were exactly where they needed to be. The only one lost and in need of a map was me. Little did I know, I was the outlier here, the unintentional fifth wheel. So much for a day at the park. This was date day, and I was crashing it.

I sat on the swing for two hours watching my sister and her best friend play fight and flirt with these two young men, who later identified themselves as Kris and Ira. Apparently, the foursome had been frolicking around parks in Pittsburgh for months now. I had no clue Patience had a boyfriend; I barely knew she liked boys. I sat there, stunned at the level of planning Patience put into this. A couple of icy stares communicated everything I needed to know. This may have been Patience's secret, but it was my crime to hide.

The ride home was quiet. LaResha's mom knew the boys by name, even asked how they were. We pulled up to our house and waved goodbye to LaResha and her mom. Patience grabbed my arm before I could reach the screen door.

"Hey," she said in a serious tone. "Are you gonna tell Mom about today?"

"No," I said somberly. "Why didn't you just tell me what you were doing before? I looked stupid, just sitting there like that!"

I meant that. I wasn't going to tell my parents on Patience. Granted, I was pissed that she played me, and so unapologetically so. But secrecy was safety in our household, and I wasn't pissed enough to want her hurt, which I had no doubt Dorothy would do. She looked at me with irritation, almost like she was annoyed by my annoyance.

"Because Arah." She sighed as she removed her huge hoop earrings, rushing as my mother unlocked the top lock. "You just wouldn't understand."

CHAPTER 6

FAST ASS GIRLS

A JOURNAL ENTRY ON JUDGEMENT

I never got the sex talk from my parents. I strongly doubt I'm the only one. Like in many other minority households, sex was a sensitive subject around our house, despite a bunch of kids being evidence of a ton of it happening. I learned about sex from a friend in the sixth grade. Her name was Mara Greene. We went to summer camp together and waited at the same bus stop in the mornings. Over time, she and I became friends. And as familiarity formed, we began spending all our free time together. We grew more comfortable with one another as the summer months passed. Over time, our conversations sunk just below the surface, our gab grew a little more grown-up, if you will.

Mara was naturally bubbly, super outgoing. She had a laugh you could pick out of a lineup. To this day, I can hear her high-pitched "Hi, Ms. Dorothy!" in my head. My mother grew to adore her larger-than-life personality and grew quite fond of Mara's mother as well, a far more reserved rendition of my friend. Over time, my mother grew comfortable with Mara and me spending time together, even outside of summer camp hours.

"Just for a few hours," my mother would reiterate as she dropped me at Mara's doorstep, "then Ms. Greene is gonna bring you back to the house, you got me?" Of course, I did. I was not about to screw this up. My mother trusted no one, and I mean no one. There were no house visits, no birthday parties, no school dances, no eighteen and under nightclubs, no movies, no amusement parks, and absolutely no sleepovers. Mara made my mother nervous, despite her fondness. She had a personality that popped and a full figure that was equally hard to hide. In my mother's mind, Mara had all the makings of a "fast ass little girl."

She questioned whether she was safe for me to be around. Between Ms. Greene's sometimes eighteen-hour shifts and Mara's flagrantly flirtatious demeanor, something told my mother to monitor the situation closely. I knew that if anything absurd happened at Mara's, there wouldn't be another Mara's. So, I committed to making sure that nothing happened, even if something did.

Now when you're ten, ten feels a lot like twenty. And if you've ever been ten before, then you know everybody's ten is a little different. I was a lot more sheltered than Mara, who knew way more about grown-up things than I did. I attributed that to her being the eldest sibling, and for many Black girls, this comes with a limitation on the length of their adolescence. But over time, I'd learn there was a lot more to my "fast ass" friend than just advanced anatomy.

One day, we got on the subject of boyfriends. I wasn't permitted to date, which was fine by me. Mara was, and she did. She sometimes told me about it in passing, never offering an abundance of detail. But on this particular day, she decided to tell me more, specifically about her boyfriend. Mara confided in me that her burly beau was none other than a guy I knew only as Theo, the twenty-year-old best friend of her older cousin. She told me about the times he'd pick her up from school and drive them back to her mother's house where they would engage in sexual intercourse. I wasn't sure what to believe because Mara joked a lot.

That is until she offered to prove it to me, and I boldly called her bluff. In an instant, Mara retrieved an old orange shoebox from beneath the bunk bed, opening the lid to reveal a collection of used condoms, each knotted to contain its contents. I'd never seen one in real life, so I had no clue what distinguished a used one from a new one. Mara grabbed one of the condoms and pretended to toss it in my direction. "It's not nasty," she parroted without provocation. "It's natural." I had no response to offer her. I just stared as she playfully picked at the condoms, one by one.

"What are you keeping all those for?" I asked, if for no other reason than to move the awkward conversation along. I had a dinosaur Giga Pet dying of starvation back home that I desperately needed to tend to. That's how out of my medium this conversation had moved.

"For when I wanna get pregnant," Mara explained. "He always yells at me to flush them, so my mom doesn't see them, but I hide it in a tissue till he leaves," Mara explained. The room fell quiet.

"Don't say nothing, okay?"

"Okay," I agreed, watching her wiggle the box of bundled condoms back under her twin-sized trundle. Mara wasn't a fast ass little girl, but that was the reputation her victimization would earn her. I feared that once word reached my mother, not only would I lose my friend, I'd also lose my mother's faith. I knew little about sex, only that it was painful and strictly reserved for married people and prostitutes, of which Mara was neither.

I did not know the imbalance of power between adults and children, women, and men. Hardly a handle on molestation, nor a proper perception of pedophilia. What I knew was that I was no stranger to the sexual advances of adult men. I knew what not to wear when we entertained male guests; I knew not to sit on any laps and to hug men from the side. I learned to cross my legs at the ankle and not wear colored nail polish to give anyone the wrong impression. They raised me in preparation to become prey, burdened by my birth alone. Had no one taught Mara how to maneuver around a man's erection?

Mara was no victim in this. At least, that's what my mother would've said. According to her, there were two types of girls in the world. There were good girls, and then there were the short-skirt-wearing, hoop earring-sporting, lip-smacking, neck-rolling fast ass girls. Those girls went out looking for attention, and boy, did they find it. Those girls, those fast ass girls, they didn't mind their mothers or their manners, probably didn't know their daddies, and didn't deal in decency and tact. Those girls, girls like Mara, deserved whatever came to them, whatever the whatever looked like.

At the time, I believed that my secrecy served a noble purpose. That purpose was the preservation of my friend's reputation, whatever little reputation she had earned at that age. Without fully understanding why, I knew the bulk of the blame for this predicament would fall on Mara, all eighty pounds of her. I know now how ridiculous it is to blame a 10-year-old for the sexual perversion of an adult male. I know now what it means to grow up in a culture that views both femininity and sexuality as sin.

Now I know that my friend was preyed upon; her hypersexuality and attention-seeking behaviors were symptoms of a much bigger issue. The adults in our lives chose not to see those signs beyond their correlation to some silly scripture. I know now that those adults, including my mother, were wrong. But back then, I found myself captured by curiosity.

My visits to Mara's continued. At first, our sexual exploration stayed somewhat civil. Mara would share stories of her "significant others." There were two before Theo, all of them over the age of eighteen. Over time, the conversation curved towards me. Mara became curious as to my maturation as a young girl. I hadn't yet begun puberty and wouldn't for another seven years. Mara, on the other hand, was way ahead of the game. She offered to help me learn how to be loved by a man. She warned me that it could sometimes be painful, but the real pleasure was in knowing that you pleased your partner. At least, that's what they'd told her.

One day, Mara sat me down and offered to show me a video she found in her dad's stash. I kid you not; *69 Cum Shots* was sprawled across the VHS case. "What's this?" I asked, noting that I was joining her three younger siblings in the sitting room, the youngest of whom was six.

"You'll see." Mara smiled as she pushed the tape into her mother's expensive entertainment center. She ploppeddown on the couch beside me. Like clockwork, her babysister leaned back and covered her eyes.

As the film began, it appeared normal. A man in a cable company uniform approached the front stairs of a suburban home. He knocked on the door, announcing himself, and a woman in a red robe answered the door. She invited him in, leading him to a bedroom in the back of the home. From there, they briefly exchanged a few words before the woman began to disrobe in front of the gentleman. I looked over at Mara, whose attention was entirely on the screen. Her twin brothers, too, looked intently at the television screen. The youngest of the crew kept her eyes covered. "Mara, what is this?" I asked. "I'm not allowed to watch Rated-R movies."

Before Mara could respond, I glanced back at the television to find the pair performing oral sex on one another. "Mara, what is this?" I exclaimed. "Just watch it," the younger of the twins chimed in. They'd seen this before, all of them. I looked back at the television to find the couple now engaged in full-on sexual intercourse. I began to fiddle with my hands, my eyes darting back and forth. I didn't know the ins and outs of what was happening, but I knew I was not supposed to be watching this. I could barely watch kissing scenes without my mother going berserk. I knew I was not supposed to be watching this, so why couldn't I look away?

I had a million and one questions. Was this what Theo had been doing to Mara? And if so, was she ever going to be okay? Why was the woman screaming so loudly? Were these now multiple men trying to murder her? Why would anyone want these things done to them? My mother included! And what the hell was wrong with my dad?! Was this how humans were made? And why the hell did I feel so damn funny?

I was experiencing sexual arousal, a concept I had no comprehension of. I didn't know the birds from the bees, barely knowing all the functions of my female form, but my brain responded to the sexually explicit stimuli the best way it knew how by hitting the hormone switch. When erotic imagery infiltrates the mind, it responds by releasing one big dose of dopamine, the brain's feel-good guy. Over time, the brain correlates these positive feelings with the consumption of this explicit imagery, even seeking them to continually source said feelings.

Despite my learned disgust, my body was intrigued. I left Mara's house different that day. I couldn't get the images out of my mind. I had all but accepted that my curiosity would kill me, especially if my mother found out. I had to make sense of what I'd just watched, but how? Asking my parents was entirely out of the question. There wasn't a book I could borrow without raising red flags, and phoning a friend is what got me into this mess in the first place.

And then it came to me; I would use my school computer lab to sort this situation all out. They were typically unattended and packed wall-to-wall with colorful iMac G3's, one of the perks of attending a prestigious private school. There I delved into the wonderful world of pornography for research purposes, of course. And so, I did, day after day, day in and day out, soaking in some of the most sordid images the internet offered, committing never to tell a soul. Something I was already good at.

CHAPTER 7

XXX

A JOURNAL ENTRY ON ADDICTION

My addiction grew aggressively over the school year and well into the spring. Porn had shown me everything I needed to know about sex. I knew for certain sex was not something I wanted, not now, not ever. I had witnessed enough slapping, sucking, licking, and unloading to last me a lifetime. It was a no for me, indefinitely. Grown-ups were gross. My parents were not exempt from that, and I didn't understand why any friend of mine would engage in such an outrageous adult activity. I began associating sex with death, believing that it could cost me my life if a man were ever too aggressive with me. The thought of being penetrated petrified me. Yet, I could not stop watching.

Every day, after lunch, I skipped recess to relax in the computer lab. Once it emptied, I'd shut the door and park at my favorite corner cube, plug my headphones in and prepare to get horny. I didn't have a word for the freaky feeling at the time, although I often felt conflicted by it. The amount of shame wasn't anywhere near the level of satisfaction it offered. I looked forward to the feeling that watching porn gave me: the thrill, the repulsiveness, the excitement of the final scene. I was a full-blown porn addict and didn't even know it.

There's an undeniable link between addiction and trauma. Too often, conversations surrounding the phenomenon focus almost exclusively on addiction as it presents in adults, but make no mistake, addiction affects children in some of the same ways. Despite what many adults want to think, trauma doesn't wait til adulthood to do damage. Trauma takes a toll on our brains immediately, altering its chemical makeup and composition with each excruciating episode.

But what does trauma look like when you're ten, twelve, or even sixteen. It looks no different from what we might expect trauma to look like in an adult. Trauma is any overwhelmingly painful and unavoidable experience. It occurs within our bodies when we encounter deeply distressing incidents. When we go through things that exceed or overwhelm our ability to function or move forward, we consider those experiences to be traumatic. The death of a loved one can fall within that category, particularly unexpected or unexplained deaths. Car accidents can be traumatic, as can natural disasters. Trauma is an unavoidable part of life, a shared component of the human experience, but not all traumas are created equally.

The community I came from condoned certain kinds of traumas even when they were known to cause casualties. Various forms of community violence, physical abuse, and corporal punishment within families, even early childhood trauma, to a certain extent, were believed to be beneficial to the young victims, strengthening them in a sense. And while other forms of traumatic dysfunction, like domestic violence and sexual abuse, were morally deemed indefensible, they were condemned quietly, if at all, often with special consideration for the perpetrator's reputation.

Older women passed out temper management techniques like communion crackers. Each of them offering advice for maneuvering around dangerous men. "You just got to let them men calm down when they get like that," Ms. Neil would explain to my mother after another one of her son's public performances, this one ending in three broken car windows. "You know how they get when you make them mad," she warned. My mother couldn't have agreed more.

By the summer of my eighth-grade year, I had witnessed my fair share of trauma, community violence, sudden death, sexual abuse, bullying, poverty, family dysfunction, social terrorism, you name it. My body had become accustomed to the input. The ring of gunshots no longer lingered in my mind after midnight. My heart stopped racing when fights broke out in my presence. My mother attributed this to my resilience. In her opinion, kids could survive anything. I was becoming increasingly acclimated to my unstable environment. My brain was slowly rewiring itself to withstand additional incidents. The day-to-day trauma felt less like trauma as time went by. I was successfully becoming desensitized to my surroundings.

When trauma is ongoing, the brain becomes burdened by the high levels of stress. The overload has a shrinking effect on the prefrontal cortex, the area of the brain that regulates personality, decision-making, and social behavior, among other things. The ongoing stress swells the amygdala, the brain's area responsible for emotional processing, making it more susceptible to future stressors. These changes to the brain's landscape have lasting effects, which research says leads to stress-induced psychological impairments like depression, anxiety, and addiction.

Most of the kids I knew were already addicted to something: drugs, alcohol, pills, food, sex. We were all coping with our ongoing trauma, the trauma of being Black, broke, and born in America. Our brains were thirsty for anything that felt good, immune to the cost of consequence. Feeding our addictions meant finding pleasure in an otherwise painful existence, albeit temporary. We could care less about the cost.

Summer came, and access was limited. I was a fiend without a supply. Poverty and a lack of internet access were forcing me to kick the can cold turkey, still susceptible to the effects of my trauma. Unbeknownst to me, my brain was now hard-wired to hunt for that feel-good feeling. After the next hormonal high, I was predisposed to these compulsive practices, thanks to the structural disruptions my brain's mainframe had undergone.

My mother was right about one thing; I was buoyant, that's for sure. But I wasn't bulletproof, and time hadn't healed much. Without my regular relief, I needed a new numbing agent, and fate would help me find one.

It was a random girl in the sixth grade who introduced me to the wonderful world of self-mutilation. She was a cutter who used to camp out in the same computer lab that housed my sordid sex secrets. With her CD player playing whatever industrial rock record doubled as the soundtrack to her sadness, she sat wrapped in a huge gray uniform hoodie, ritually, meticulously, dragging a straight razor across her forearm.

Over time, our repeated run-ins revealed the nature of our dire need for the shared space, though we hardly spoke a word. I fed my addiction on one side of the screen; she fed hers on the other. And while I'd plucked a hair or two in frustration, I was never fully sold on self-injury being my thing. Anytime the thought crept its way inside my conscience, I heard my mother hollering in the back of my mind, "I don't know no Black people that do that type of mess." I didn't either. But a stressful summer would leave me desperate and reeling for a release. Soon, cutting would provide the perfect escape.

I enjoyed the summer months, despite the uptick in trauma exposure it meant for myself and most inner-city kids. The shootings were out of control, but the noise pollution was a small price to pay. Summer camp was where I shined. There I felt seen and considered. They always asked me for my input and encouraged me to take on new tasks, not to mention, being a year younger than the other camp counselors gave me an edge. People presumed I was a year ahead for academic reasons, and I wasn't about to tell them they were wrong.

It was my first real job. For the first time, I would be earning an actual paycheck. I had the amount all figured out; $3,000 in cold hard cash. Well, more like hard-pressed paper. I circled the two semi-summer pay dates in purple pen; I was going to buy my first pair of name brand shoes with that money. Maybe some butter-colored Timberland boots to make up for my mother's Payless ones she made me wear all winter. A F.U.B.U. T-shirt or two with the matching sweats, if I had anything left over. I didn't know how much any of this stuff cost. It could've been the whole check; I didn't care.

My entire family knew about my summer job. I had talked about it all year long. Everyone had their suggestion for what I should do with my new-found fortune. "Make sure you put it inside your savings. Eh heh," my father advised. "It's good to have small-small money saved for your chips and candies. You know how you like your treats," he said and smiled. I would always be a little girl in his eyes.

My mother's advice was simple. "Don't go around telling everybody you about to get some money," she warned me. "Soon, everybody gone have they hand out and you know you don't know how to say no." My mother was right. Saying 'no' was a struggle for me. Time, effort, energy, attention, you name it, if I had it to give, it was yours. Hell, even if I didn't. That bit of advice was in one ear and out the other. The same week, I would agree to loan my oldest sister, Temi, $1,000 to furnish my unborn niece's nursery.

"I promise I'll give it back at the end of the month when her daddy gets paid," she said as she applied the pressure. I wanted to believe her fully, but to be honest, I didn't. She had a history of defaulting on debts. That part of her past was no secret. But, no was not easy for me; everyone knew that. I reluctantly agreed to the two-week repayment term as presented. Quietly hoping I wouldn't come to regret it.

"Do me a favor. Don't tell Mom and Dad you loaned me this money," Temi said as we exchanged the cash on payday. "Ok, I won't," I agreed. Yet another secret I needed to keep. She hugged me tightly, thanking me for my generosity and promising to repay. I wanted to believe her; I did. But Temi had a track record. I was about to find out firsthand just how true the rumors were.

Our agreed-upon repayment date came and went, and I hadn't heard a word from Temi. By the middle of the month, I was beginning to think that maybe she had forgotten that she owed me. I'd all but blown through the $500 that remained from my paycheck. Who knew how quickly treating your family to fast food twice a week and ordering butter-colored Timberlands from the Eastbay catalog could add up? I was broke. Luckily, Temi still owed me. But now that it was time for her to pay me back, I felt I'd hit a brick wall. She wasn't even dodging me; she was simply behaving as though the debt, and me, didn't exist.

I shook myself back to my senses. Of course, she still owed me. No way in hell she'd forgotten that fast. To avoid confrontation, I waited one day until Patience left for her boyfriend's mother's house, some six or so miles down the road. Thinking a phone call might go over better.

"Hey T!" I said as she answered the phone. "It's Arah."

"Hey, babe! What's up?"

"I was wondering if you had that money I let you hold?"

"What money?" Temi replied.

"The money you said you needed for Hope's nursery."

"Oh, that money," she said, sucking her teeth.

"I forgot all about that little money."

That's easy for you to say, I said to myself. *It wasn't your money, to begin with.*

"I'm not gone be able to give it to you right now."

"Why not?"

"Because having a baby is expensive!" she snapped. "Do you know how much it costs to have a kid?"

"No," I responded, not seeing what any of this had to do with my money.

"Exactly."

"When do you think you can give it back then?"

I lowered my tone. I didn't understand why she was so upset with me as if I had done something wrong.

"Arah, you not gone chase me around stressing me out about no goddamn money now, knowing damn well I do for everybody up in that house. But that's okay. You'll get your lil money back by the end of the month," she scathed as she slammed the telephone down. I was devastated. *I'm never gonna see that money again*, I said to myself, slowly setting down the receiver.

I didn't bring it up again for a few more weeks. The end of the month came and went with still no sign of repayment. Temi continued to come in and out of my parents' house in her normal nomadic fashion. Sometimes making meaningless small talk with me during visits. I guessed she had forgotten again, and by forgotten, I'm speaking facetiously, of course. It wasn't Temi's memory that was the problem; it was her poor money management that threatened to thwart our little arrangement. Temi didn't have that money, at least not anymore. Getting her to admit that would be the real challenge.

As I sat contemplating my next move, my father called for me from his prayer room. And yes, the man needed an entire room just to perfect his practice of religion. I peeked in to see him still on his knees. "Yes,

Sir?" I whispered. He hated interruptions in the middle of meditation, so I was curious about the timing of his call.

He peeked at me with one eye. "Nne," he called. "Have a seat." I walked in and sat on the two-seat sofa. "Yes, Sir," I said again, intending to keep things brief.

My father's prayer space was what you might call just a tad bit creepy. Porcelain statues of Catholic saints, religious relics from around the world, and a picture of an old white man moonlighting as a messiah lined the light blue walls. It felt as if you were being watched, standing in front of a judgmental jury of biblical B-listers. Nothing was more nerve-racking than getting grilled in my father's prayer room. It was impossible to tell a lie with all those eerie eyes on you. Well, almost.

"I want to ask you something," my father spoke slowly. "We have situation back home with your uncle Emmanuel. His wife, your Aunt Chidera, has fallen sick with cancer." "Oh, no!" I interrupted. "Yes, he call us this morning to tell us this news," my father continued.

"While she's in hospital, you know they have small baby, eh heh, and that baby will need caring for. So, they want to hire a small house to help look after the baby and be tending to auntie while she receives her treatment. You know these things cost." I nodded my head in agreement. "Eh heh. Back home, you're lucky to get regular pay where you can be paying your bills small-small. And there's no credit, no month-to-month business, so either you pay everything upfront, or you just don't have. Not like here where everything is I.O.U."

He cracked a smile, and I smiled back. "So, your momma and I discuss it, and we're going to send some money home. I spoke with your older siblings, who have agreed to each be sending their tithe. And now that you're receiving small paycheck, you can be sending your tithe too. How does that sound? Good?" he asked with a smile on his face.

My body tensed up. It felt like the room was about to catch fire; my face was so hot. I lied anyway.

"Yes, Daddy, that sounds good."

"Very good," he replied. "Give your tithe money to your momma, and she will put it with the other money to send."

"Yes, Sir," I lied again. I got up from the sofa, surprised I didn't leave a life-sized sweat stain. My heart pounded violently. I'd just committed myself to more stress, more secrets, more sneaking around, and I only had myself to blame.

Temi wasn't going to give me that money back, not without a fight, at least, perhaps even a physical one. And with the rest of my small salary scheduled to mail out at the end of our summer session, I was out of dollars indefinitely and quickly running out of ways to hide it.

"Arah!" my mother hollered from downstairs. "Come here, real quick!" The walls were closing in on me quickly. If this was another inquiry about money, my head was going to burst. I slowly trotted to the landing at the top of the stairs. "Yes, Ma'am," I answered her. "Bring me your tithe money for Uncle Emma," she said as she scrummaged through her purse, looking for car keys. "I'm gonna put it all in the bank so Dad can send everything to Africa at one time."

"Ok," I said, slumping back up the stairs. You would think my mother wasn't married to a no-nonsense Nigerian man the way she looped all of Africa together like a tiny European town. Some old habits never died. I walked into my room and melted onto my mattress. I lay there, struggling to comprehend how I'd gotten myself into such a sunken situation. The stress was overwhelming me. It was only a matter of time before the news broke that I was flat broke, and once my parents found out why, that would be the end of me. Everyone knew not to loan money to Temi. What the hell was I thinking?

"Arah!" my mother called out from the stairs. "Yes, Ma'am?" I answered. At this point, I was just stalling the inevitable. I could feel a knot forming in my stomach. I was making myself sick with stress. "Yes, Ma'am?" I yelled again, this time, forcing myself to confront the confrontation. *Just tell her you don't have it. She's gonna find out eventually, anyway.*

Once again, I reached the landing at the top of the stairs, and there she stood at the bottom of them, arms crossed tightly.

"Arah."

"Yes, Ma'am?"

"I'm waiting on you."

"Oh, okay. Sorry."

I turned around and forced a faux jog back to my room. For the second time, I drowned myself in my duvet. I thought maybe she might just leave, cut her wait time, and take off without my contribution. But the chances of that happening were highly unlikely.

"Now, I know damn well!" my mother shouted before shoving my bedroom door open, scaring me shitless.

"Arah, get up out that bed!" she yelled. I quickly did as I was told.

"Where is this tithe money so I can go? The bank close at 4," she said excitedly. I didn't have an answer. I just sat there staring at my hands.

"I'm talking to you," she emphasized after a brief wait.

"I gave it to Temi," I mumbled.

"You did what?!"

"I gave it to Temi, but she was supposed to give it back!" I said as tears streamed down my face. "You gave it to Temi?! How much did you give her?"

"$1,000."

My mother couldn't believe her ears.

"How long did you plan on pretending you still had it?"

"I guess until she paid it back," I answered honestly.

My mother was stunned. She was stupefied. It was the one thing she told me not to do with my money, and I did it anyway.

"Well, you can explain to your father why you don't have your tithe money," she began. "And that little camp trip you have coming up, you can kiss that goodbye. Now, I could make Temi give you your money back, but that's the price for being disobedient. Bet you wish you'd listened now, don't you?"

"Yes, Ma'am," I said in-between sniffs.

My mother left the room enraged. I was devastated about missing the fishing trip and even more mortified by the fact that I had to have this conversation again.

The next day, I went to camp, not looking forward to breaking the bad news to my boss. I wouldn't be able to chaperone the fishing trip for family reasons, which was another white lie. It just so happened they had a secondary station for me to man. The seventh-grade farewell formal was happening on the same day, and a few counselors were needed to chaperone that too; I quickly added myself to the schedule.

That evening my father had a talk with me about my missing money. Despite claiming the news was mine to share, my mother took the liberty of letting my dad in on our little secret. Only slightly disappointed, my father was more impressed than anything else. It was my dishonesty he took issue with. He found it noble that I was so willing to help the family but warned me gently of the dangers of being too generous.

Neither of my parents was willing to intervene. "Banks spend millions teaching their employees to say 'no.' Now you know why," my dad laughed. This time, I didn't join him. I didn't understand my parents' refusal to rectify the situation between my sister and me. Not only were we over a decade apart, but she had a history of doing the same thing to other siblings, making the behavior not only premeditated but predatory.

When parents fail to protect their children from one another, which certain situations call for, it creates environmental instability between siblings. It's the adults' responsibility in the home to model what is appropriate behavior and what is not. When children violate the boundaries meant to keep the family members safe, it is essential that a parent step in to rectify that wrong. And this is not to override their children's autonomy or deny them the ability to demonstrate healthy conflict resolution themselves. It's to ensure that no one is detrimentally damaged in the process.

Taking advantage of the pre-existing power differential between us with her being the eldest of us all, Temi played on my empathy and inexperience to persuade me to pony up my paycheck. Temi felt owed for being the oldest after all her adolescent years spent tending to toddlers. There was a good amount of animosity that existed between Temi and the rest of us. That unaddressed dynamic of the overworked eldest child would play out repeatedly, revealing unearthed resentment on recurring occurrences.

That next day, I woke up feeling defunct. I dressed for camp, as usual, opting for a lime green on lime green short set. I had forgotten all about the formal dance that day. I had way too much on my mind. I got to work and was immediately reminded of the day's date. Fishing rods lined the foyer where eighth-grade field trip attendees would later congregate. "Arah, you didn't dress up!" one of the other counselors called out to me from the balcony. *Oh, fuck! It is Friday.* And Friday was the day of the seventh-grade formal. I couldn't chaperone the dance in these vomit-colored clothes. "I'm changing later," I called back. "Oh, okay. Cool!" she said, sounding relieved—yet another lie.

But it didn't have to be. I bolted to the office and dialed my house. The house phone rang twice. My mother picked up on the third ring.

"Hey, Mom!" I said excitedly. This was a shot in the dark, but what the hell.

"What's wrong?" she replied, which was her routine.

"Nothing, Mom. I just wanted to ask you a favor."

"What's that?"

"You think you could bring me some dress clothes?"

"Bring you some dress clothes?!"

"Yes, Mom. I forgot that today is the seventh-grade formal, and they asked me to chaperone. But I have on a tank top and shorts."

"I'm not tryna drive all the way up there to drop off no clothes, Arah."

"Mom, please! I don't have any other options."

"Let me think about it."

"Mom…"

"I said I gotta think about it! What time is the formal?"

"It starts at 2 p.m."

"Well, call me back at around 12."

"Mom, please answer the phone."

"I will. Call me back around 12."

"Okay," I sighed heavily.

I knew better than to get my hopes up. Still, I kept my fingers crossed.

The morning moved like rush hour traffic.

I watched the clock intently, waiting for the moment of truth. I could hardly eat lunch; I was so sick with anticipation. "Arah, where's your dress?" another counselor questioned. After a while, I grew tired of singing the same old tune.

Finally, noon rolled around. I ran to the office to find the phone occupied. It was a sick camp goer occupying the phone. I half smiled, attempting to be cordial to the kid. After all, I was still on the job.

I wanted to bum rush the little guy but refrained. After completing his call, he hopped up and headed back into the hallway as another camp goer attempted to occupy the now empty seat. I raced past the receptionist, dialed my mother as quickly as I could, and held my breath as the phone rang.

"Hello?" Patience answered.

"Hey, where's Mom?"

"She's not here."

"What do you mean she's not there?"

"I mean, she's not here."

"Well, where is she?"

"Girl, I don't know! Who are you yelling at, though?"

"Patience, this is important. Do you know when she'll be back?"

"Nope!"

"Ok, I'll call her back. Bye."

The room started to spin. *This cannot be happening.* I glanced up at the wall clock to double-check the time. My brain replayed our earlier exchange over and over. I began doubting whether I'd heard her right. I could've sworn she said noon, I said to myself again and again. I had forgotten all about the kid waiting in the doorway who eventually got the hint and headed off to class. I dialed again. "Hello?" Patience answered a second time.

"Hey, is she there?"

"Nope, not yet."

"Okay, bye."

We hung up again. It was now a quarter after twelve. I waited for ten agonizing minutes and called again. Still, no luck. Still, no Mom.

It was now half-past noon; I gave it one last shot.

"Hel..."

"Hey, is she there?"

"Nope, not yet."

One o'clock. One fifteen. We had been at it for over an hour now. I'd all but given up hope and decided to try one final time, this time for real. To my surprise, my mother answered the phone.

"Mom!" I jumped up in the chair.

"Yeah? What?" she said nonchalantly as though nothing was wrong.

"Are you coming?"

"No, Arah. Wear what you have on."

Her words felt like fire.

"Mom, I can't. I just won't be able to go."

"Well…" she said.

I have never wanted to hang up on someone so badly in my life, but I valued my life more than that.

"Okay, Mom."

"Okay."

"K, Bye."

I waited for my mother to hang up the phone first. My eyes became wet with my unshed tears. I needed to keep it together momentarily, at least until I could get far enough away from other people. I passed by the camp director in the office doorway. "Arah! What happened?" he asked, gesturing towards my lime green two-piece.

"Yeah, my mom couldn't get off of work in time to bring me a change of clothes," I lied. "Oh, no! Well, you can always hang out here in the office," he offered. I smiled to say thank you. I wasn't interested. I thought my brain might explode from the pressure. I was sad, sick, and stressed beyond belief. Did everything in my life have to happen the hard way?

I walked against the traffic as chatty camp goers headed to the gymnasium for the formal. Tears flowed down my face; I was failing to hide my frustration. I was embarrassed. I felt betrayed and abandoned. I pushed my way inside an empty art room and bawled my eyes out. I wanted to scream; I wanted to break something; to knock things on to the floor, but I couldn't. All I could do was cry. Rage was reserved for warriors, not young women.

I was undergoing an exercise in women's suffrage, learning the right way to suffocate my sorrows. I locked eyes with an X-Acto knife left lying on the desk. I picked it up and pressed it against my forearm. In an instant, blood gushed from the incision, causing me to drop the blade back on the desk. The amount of blood took me by surprise. I picked up the cutting tool a second time and sliced again, this time, applying less pressure. My brown skin slid open, revealing the fresh white flesh beneath it. The cut quickly filled with blood. I sliced again. I sliced once more. Tears fell from my face into the crime scene that was now my forearm. I cut myself and cried quietly. This was it; this was how you suffered in silence.

Television static trickled up my arm. The room fell quiet. My body felt calm. I slumped into a seat, feeling physically exhausted. My arm stained red with the residue of my unsightly deeds. I hadn't even considered how I would hide evidence of the self-inflicted attack. I scanned the room, looking for something to hide my arm in. An abandoned hoodie on the back of an easel would provide the perfect cover. I grabbed it and threw it on, hiding my face in the hood.

I don't blame my mother for pushing me past my boiling point. To be honest, my mother had a lot going on, and as an adult, it's easy to overlook the significance of something that seems less than essential, like a camp formal. We're at our best as parents when we can practice empathetic parenting, meaning putting ourselves in our child's shoes and considering that the impact of a situation may appear greater to them than we know it to be.

Missing the formal wasn't the worst thing that could've happened to me. Nor was being swindled out of

$1,000 by my sister. But the culmination of situations coupled with an inability to outwardly express my emotions and a not so supportive stressful home environment was a recipe for disaster, no matter how you sliced it. No pun intended.

Before I knew it, I was cutting every day to relieve the pressures of my everyday life—each incision releasing just enough dopamine to keep me coming back for more. I was hooked on hormones, hiding behind wristbands and long sleeve shirts in the summer. I had traded in my old addiction for a new one, one I didn't need the internet or electricity to enjoy.

CHAPTER 8

PUNCH BUGGY, NO PUNCH BACK

A JOURNAL ENTRY ON REVENGE

By the start of my ninth-grade year, Patience and I had all but grown apart. Attending two separate schools made staying connected an even bigger challenge than before. I was attending a small private all-girl school. Not having to hide my intelligence from male classmates was a huge weight off my shoulders. My graduating class was the biggest in history; a whopping forty-one young women set to walk across the stage. The Ivy league-like tuition meant girls like me were far, few, and in-between. "Scholarship" was a code word for colored, and boy, did administration love a scholarship recipient. They lumped us into a litany of promotional photos together. 'The Elysian School for Girls, where dreams and diversity thrive!" read across every printed pamphlet. It was an even exchange as far as they could tell, a top tier education for a few years of exploitation. Who in their right mind, particularly in our position, would turn that down? Certainly not our parents.

Meanwhile, Patience clung even closer to her friends. She was cutting little ole me almost completely out of the picture. She'd built quite the cool girl reputation for herself throughout high school and couldn't have me corny up the place. I hated it, but I understood. Looking back, I can say that her desire to build bonds beyond our shared bloodline was completely normal. It was natural to seek social autonomy as an adolescent, and there were healthy and unhealthy ways to go about doing that. Now, how my parents responded to our pleas for independence was the real issue. My dad's preferred approach was avoidance. My mother's, full-on fight or flight. She was petrified of teen pregnancy. It was her firm belief that girls were just harder to raise, mainly for that reason. Success was getting us all off to college without gaining any grandchildren. And she would do whatever to watch our wombs.

The more Patience attempted to explore her independence; the more my mother cracked down. Phone calls were monitored manually. Journals were jogged through, the whole nine. She had a point to prove, and you were gonna help her do it. Girls were sneaky, impossible to trust. The last thing you wanted to do was give one any wiggle room, and Dorothy Jean did not plan to let up.

Like the time Patience dodged drill practice to sneak to a neighboring school's lineup. Now for those of you who have never heard of a lineup, let me set the scene. A lineup is a school-sponsored fashion and automobile exhibition for senior students and upperclassmen attendees, friends, and family, and yes, it is as fancy as it seems. Patience and I attended private schools, so we missed out on many of young Black Pittsburgh's important social invitations. Black prom was one of them.

Now it was one thing to attend a lineup; being invited to an actual prom was another success level. And then there were levels to those invitations because not all proms were created equally. The upper echelon of Pittsburgh high school prom season, Schenley High School, and everyone knew it.

Patience didn't run in those circles, but LaResha did. She had already attended one city school prom and was scheduled to attend two winter formals and a homecoming dance. Patience felt like she was missing out, but my parents' permission meant nothing without an invitation. She and LaResha planned to fish in a more fitting pond. If you wanted an invitation to a public-school prom, you had to be where the public-school boys could see you.

It didn't take much for my mom to find out that Patience had dodged her club duties for a dip in the pre-prom pond. Practice let out early because of low attendance, and a friendly call from a friend on the team looking to chat with Patience, who was still supposed to be in practice, kinda blew up the whole scheme. Patience didn't know this.

She moseyed in after 8 p.m., which was the normal time drill practice ended. Our schools were on the other side of town, and my mother was no one's chauffeur. That meant two, sometimes three buses across town twice a day, going and coming. The commute was a crawl; our mornings started before sunrise and our evenings wrapped up after dark.

"How was practice?" my mother asked casually. A setup if I ever saw one. Now my mother had known since shortly after 5 p.m. that Patience played hooky. She pondered on that piece of information, and for hours, brewed on the perfect punishment. She presumed my sister would be dishonest, even if directly confronted with an opportunity to tell the truth. Instead, she set the scene and watched her script play out in real-time.

"Practice was good," Patience lied.

"Did Kayla's mother drop you off?"

"No, I caught the bus back."

"You should've called me. What time did you guys get done?"

Patience twisted her face. We were all thinking the same thing, called you for what? When it came to transportation, we were on our own. My mother blamed gas prices, traffic, potholes, and pollution for her fear of driving even the shortest distance, anything to hide her automobile anxiety. We all knew by now; Dorothy Jean was no one's chauffeur.

"We finished at our regular time, 7." "Anybody wait on the bus with you? You know I don't like you waiting at that Park N' Ride alone."

This was tough to watch, but I couldn't look away. The pair went back and forth for a good six minutes.

"Nne, welcome!" My dad interrupted the exchange. "Where are you returning from?"

"I had drill practice, Daddy." She continued the coverup. And why not? She was already knee-deep in shit. My dad thanked God for her safe return, prompting my mother to grab her purse from the coffee table and take off towards the staircase.

"Patience, lemme speak with you for a moment," my mother said, slowly making her way up the stairs. Patience's face flushed. She knew what time it was. We all did. But did it have to be so dramatic? Did everything?

"Okay," Patience replied, dragging herself up from the couch where she'd just cozied up.

Long story short, Patience got her ass beat. The older we got, the more beatings seemed my mother's go-to. It's not that I recall her talking to us more, but I recall being beaten less. Those damn hormones. How else was she supposed to keep our fast asses in line? My mother perceived all acts of independence as though they were spiritual attacks. She couldn't fathom Patience wanting to form a social identity of her own, not without Satan's influence, anyway. It was a slight to my mother. A sign that we were pulling away despite all she had done for us. Not on Dorothy's watch.

Patience lost what little freedom she had after the incident. As tensions grew between her and my mother, it put a strain on the entire house. Until that point, Patience occupied a parental position in the home, a common occurrence for the eldest child in the family. My mother regarded her as an adult when it suited her needs, but when it challenged her authority, she felt compelled to remind Patience of her place. She was a child, no matter how grown her body had gotten.

Patience took that out on us, seeing any and every infraction as an opportunity to get Dorothy off her back. My mother was reading her diary, and Patience was reading everyone else's. She learned the leverage of well-

140

timed tea. Even if it only distracted our dear mother for a moment, it was a moment where her every move wasn't being watched. She yearned for the freedom she'd seen her peers enjoying. Your secret was not safe with her. It wasn't personal; it was about survival.

That summer, I formed my first crush, like a real crush. His name was Blake Delmar; I met him at summer camp too. He was attending as an incoming freshman, and I was a returning junior counselor, but we were the same age because of my early academic start. Still, I'm sure somewhere upon being hired; I signed an agreement not to date the students. Not my shining moment. I can admit that.

He was quirky and into anime. The fact that he didn't seem the least bit interested in me only made me like him more. That partner preference would come back to beat my ass. When he asked for my phone number at camp commencement, I was taken aback. He had noticed me after all. I couldn't say no; I couldn't say yes either. My mom had a strict no-boys policy for phone calls. There was no way I was letting Blake call me and blow my cover. I had to be smart about this, but I couldn't let the opportunity pass.

"I'll give you my number, but you can't call my house. My mom doesn't let us talk to boys on the phone."

"But, you're in high school."

"Believe me, I know."

"Ok, well, are you gonna call me?"

"Yeah, I just can't call you all the time. But I can call you."

"Okay, so call me."

"I will." I smiled. And I intended to make good.

I was sneaking on the phone multiple nights a week to talk to Blake. We talked about everything: his family, my family, his favorite food, the proper way to pronounce mine. It was cool to him that my father was Nigerian; he even learned a few Igbo words. He was the first boy I liked that didn't dock me for being the kind of Black girl I was. I liked Blake a lot for that. It felt like he liked me too.

I signed up for fall camp to be close to him during the school year. Why not? I was being paid to parlay with my new boo. Blake would be my first kiss too. It was trash, stuffed in a dirty stairwell that connected to the city bus line. I didn't mind; he didn't either. Blake was kinda cool. I liked Blake a lot.

About five months into official girlfriend/boyfriend status, Blake invited me to attend a luncheon with him and his family. He wanted to introduce me to his parents and older sister. The thought almost made me vomit. Before he could finish formally inviting me, I had a sound list of excuses at my disposal. There was no way this meeting was going to happen. The thought of meeting someone's parents paralyzed me. It was the fact that meeting his family would likely bring my own into question. The further away we stayed from each other's families, the better off we would both be. He didn't exist in my family. I needed it to stay that way.

But the luncheon was far away enough that I could retract my commitment to attend. So, I told him I would go, that's what a good girlfriend would do. The luncheon was the furthest thing from my mind, especially after my cousin invited us to her annual athletes' brunch. Eventually, I told Blake about my conflict of interest; he seemed to understand. I was off the hook for meeting the parents, and Blake and I were still going strong. Mission accomplished. Or so I thought.

On the day of the brunch, my dad decided he had no interest in attending an award ceremony that wasn't celebrating scholarship. After all, he hadn't come all this way to America to applaud athletics. He was dramatic like that. Frustrated, my mom opted out of the outing altogether. "I'll drop you two off, and Aunt Sheila can bring you back afterward," my mother arranged. I didn't complain. I liked that arrangement better anyway.

"Punch buggy, no punch back!" Patience sang as she swatted me from the front seat. My mother took the scenic route everywhere, petrified of Pittsburgh's busy highways. We arrived as scheduled, dressed in our brunch best. My cousin Femi and her mother, Aunt Sheila, met us at the door. Femi was my play cousin. Our fathers met at the University of Pittsburgh, where the pair formed a friendship based on their shared West African identity. You could count the West Africans in Pittsburgh on the one hand. And when you were a stranger in an unfamiliar place, a familiar face felt a lot like family. Femi and her family were family.

The four of us exchanged hugs. We didn't get to see

each other that often. Femi and her family lived in one of the suburbs outside the city. Her dad was an architect, a big one at that. Photos of his downtown designs decorated the gates of our local airport. He was a big deal, and he knew it. Femi and her sisters had the best of everything. Trips to her old house were like mall missions. Everything was new with tags, name brand, no hand-me-downs: designer bags and expensive boutique clothes. Ms. Sheila's wardrobe was overrun with silk robes and hand-sewn garments, gold, and too many gowns to close the sliding door. Femi lived a good life. Well, used to, anyway.

It turns out all that glittered wasn't worth a damn. Femi's dad had a hard time keeping his vows. By the time we hit high school, Uncle Robert had peeled off with his side piece, leaving Aunt Sheila and the girls to fend for themselves. After a short stint in a homeless shelter, Aunt Sheila rented a two-bedroom apartment eight miles down the road from her former estate; the one Uncle Robert refurnished for his new pregnant fiancée. It kept Femi and her sisters from switching school districts, which was the only piece of their past life Aunt Sheila could keep. So, I wasn't surprised by his absence. When had he ever really been present?

Each of us was handed a program and shown to our table tucked to the left of the stage. Shortly after that, another family joined us. As we engaged in small talk, I flipped through the pages of the program. It looked like a lot of Black private school student-athletes were being honored that day. This was another one of those things that private schools stripped from its Black students; the opportunity to excel in the athletic experience amongst their peers, which contrary to popular belief, makes a big difference.

The first time anyone called me the "N-word" was on the lacrosse field in the middle of a scrimmage. Femi, who played field hockey, shared similar experiences. We were often the only Black girls on the field, playing against privileged private school white girls who hated losing and hated losing to "ghetto" girls like us even more. That was their go-to dig.

Every chance they got, they needed to remind us that it was their pity that put us there, not our purpose. Playing in an environment like that made it tough to consider

146

yourself a part of the team, particularly when teammates ignored the abuse you endured both on and off the field. We needed more Black spaces like this brunch for Black athletes in my city, who were forced to figure out sportsmanship, dedication, and devotion without a caring community's support.

We chatted it up at the table. The waitress came by to take our orders, which was nice. I played like I wasn't impressed. I was oh so overly impressed. I watched Femi and Aunt Sheila joke with each other, trying each other's drinks. I envied their closeness. Even during the stressful dissolution of her marriage, Aunt Sheila always made time to support Femi. I wanted a mother like that. If I'm being honest, I often wished it were her.

Right as I had excused myself to go to the ladies' room, I felt a hand press against my shoulder, sealing me to my seat. The heads at the table whipped in my direction; I looked up to see who was behind me. It was Blake, my boyfriend, whom I told I was too busy to attend this very event. My eyes widened, and I mean ridiculously wide. I could feel the sweat beads forming at the nape of my neck.

"Hey!" I said, sounding startled.

"Hey! What are you doing here?"

"I didn't know my cousin's brunch was the same thing as your luncheon," I halfway explained. I wasn't lying.

"Oh, wow! That's crazy! Is this your mom?" he asked, attempting to make introductions. "No, this is my aunt Sheila, this is my cousin Femi, and that's my big sister Patience." My sister sat silently as Blake went around the table, shaking hands. I had to get him the hell away from here, but how?

"Hey! Where are you sitting?" I said, standing up from the table.

"Right over there." He gestured across the room to a large table in the center of the banquet hall.

"I was just about to run to the bathroom, but when I get back, I'll come introduce myself to your table."

"Okay, cool," he said as he pulled me in for a hug. I could have fainted. This was my nightmare. How the hell did luck run this low?

As our chests parted, I could see Patience holding hers, not even attempting to hide the look of shock on her face. I hurried off to the restroom, crammed myself into the smallest stall and bawled my eyes out. I would have stayed in that stall all night had I not thought it made things worse. I fixed my glasses back over my face and made a beeline for the back entrance of the hall. If I could make it through today, it would be a miracle. But first, I had to dodge the Delmars.

I crept up behind Blake's chair, gripping him by the shoulders. "Good Afternoon!" I greeted the table. To which Blake responded by hopping up from his chair. "Oh, hey!" He hugged me again. "Mom, Dad, this is Arah. Brandi, this is Arah, Arah, this is my sister Brandi." I went around the table, exchanging pleasantries with everyone. Mrs. Delmar squeezed me tightly. "It's so nice to meet you!" she squealed. "The pleasure is all mine." I blushed.

"Come on over here and sit down with us!" Blake's dad ushered towards me.

"Pops, she's sitting with her family," Blake interjected.

"Oh, come on. She can sit with us for a few minutes. I'm sure they'll be there when she gets back. Mrs. Delmar pulled an empty chair up to the table as Mr. Delmar summoned me to their side. I did as I was told and took the seat, body flowing full of nerves. I needed to get back to my table. Sitting down was not a part of the plan. But I didn't want my dilemma to be too obvious.

"We've heard a lot about you," Mr. Delmar gushed. "We sure have. It's not often Blakey brings up a girl," his wife chimed in. "Good things, I hope," I replied, quickly glancing down at my watch. We all joined in a chuckle. My clock was ticking.

"What school do you go to again?" Brandi blurted out. "Elysian, right? I know like everybody at Elysian."

"Yeah, I've been there since the sixth grade." "You like going to an all-girl school? I think it's a little weird."

"Shut up, Brandi!" Blake yelled. I didn't mind. Everyone I met said the same thing.

"You know what? I like it," I responded while smiling. "I thought the same thing before I became a student."

Brandi was no bigger or better than any other mean girl I'd met. Her jabs did nothing to throw me off my game. Besides, she was doing her big sister duty, giving her brother's girlfriend the once over, and I couldn't fault her for that.

"You know, Blake tells us you're Nigerian." "Yes, Ma'am. My father is from Enugu State."

"We think that is a beautiful thing," Mrs. Delmar exclaimed. "We've been learning a lot about Kwanzaa at our church; we think the culture is just lovely." I thanked her, even though Kwanzaa had more to do with Kansas than it did Nigeria. Your boyfriend's mother was one person who didn't need permission to be wrong. Besides, I was used to the ignorance.

The pleasantries bounced back and forth before I realized I had overstayed my stay. "If you all don't mind, I'm gonna head back to my table," I explained. "My cousin goes onstage soon, and I promised my mom I'd get some good pictures." Everyone seemed to understand. Blake and his dad stood to excuse me from the table as I hugged everyone on the way out. "Don't forget to stop by before you go so we can meet your family," Mrs. Delmar demanded. I smiled. There was no way that was happening. I agreed, anyway.

I slid back into my seat. Patience's eyes were locked on mine. "Who was that?" she asked. "My friend from summer camp," I said confidently. "Don't let me find out you gotta little boyfriend, Arah," Aunt Sheila joked at the wrong time. Femi coughed with laughter. The unlikelihood of the whole thing tickled them pink. Everyone knew Dorothy did not play about her daughters dating. I was breaking the cardinal rule, whatever I called myself doing with Blake.

The rest of the luncheon went off without a hitch. Some subtle stalking and well-planned waving kept me in good graces with the Delmar gang, and beyond the awkward stares from Patience, no one else seemed to notice anything out of the ordinary. We said our goodbyes to other attendees, slowly making our way through the parking lot. Just then, Blake runs up from between two parked cars and grabs hold of me, kissing me on my cheek in front of everyone. Aunt Sheila gasped. "I'll talk to you later, Arah. You ladies have a good evening!" He waved to my family, disappearing between two parked vehicles. The gig was up. I couldn't lie any longer. Blake was more than just some camp buddy. No friend was putting forth that amount of effort.

During the drive home, I thought about what my murder might look like. Would my mom starve me to death for my fast ass indiscretion? Would she send me packing on a one-way flight to the village where I would surely perish from my city girl ways? I didn't know how it would happen, but I had no hope to survive the next twenty-four hours, if not for my big sister's grace.

Patience and I rode in silence the whole way. Aunt Sheila and Femi sang songs from the front seat. It was the longest, most agonizing sixteen miles of my life. I took my time climbing out of the car. This must have been what walking the plank felt like. As we approached our front porch, Patience turned to me and stopped. "Was that boy your boyfriend?" she asked calmly. "If he was, you can tell me." We stood there for a while. I wasn't sure if she was sincere. I wanted to trust my sister. I wanted to tell her my secrets. It was lonely not having her to rely on, in a partner way, not a parent way.

"Yeah, he is," I caved.

"That's nice." She sighed. "He's cute, too."

"Thanks." I chuckled, feeling relieved for the first time all day.

"Please don't tell Mom and Dad," I pleaded. "I never told Mom about Ira, or Von, or any of your other little friends," I said sarcastically. We laughed a little more. It felt familiar. I missed my sister. This felt like the beginning of something good.

We walked in the house in good spirits; I had high hopes.

"How'd it go, girls?" my mom asked.

"It went good!"

"How's Femi doing?"

"She's doing great."

"Did her daddy show up?"

"No, he wasn't there."

My mother shook her head. We all knew Uncle Robert wasn't shit.

"A lot of people were there," Patience continued.

"You remember Ms. Alteri, our old teacher from Temple Christian Academy?"

"Ooh Yeah!"

"And Ms. Murphy and her daughter were there. She got an award for Basketball Coach of the Year."

"Oh, wow, I forgot Ms. Murphy left Macklin Middle School."

"Yep. And Arah's friend was there too."

"Arah's friend? Which friend, Arah?" I froze. No way Patience

154

played me again. I couldn't think quickly enough. "Huh?" I said, instead. "Which friend?" she asked again. I looked at Patience, who was smiling ear to ear. In a flash, I saw my life end. "Oh yeah, Mom, I meant to tell you." Patience plopped down next to her. "Arah has a boyfriend."

CHAPTER 9

LIGHT-SKINNED LADY

A JOURNAL ENTRY ON MEAN GIRLS

My relationship with Patience never recovered. Things worsened when she went to college, if you can imagine that. In my senior year of high school, shit hit the fan. My parents pushed Patience to attend the University of Pittsburgh, the very place their paths crossed. Despite her acceptance to some other impressive universities, some that came with a significant amount of financial assistance, my parents felt nothing topped the nostalgia or the University of Pittsburgh's nearness. She hated them for their decision, at least momentarily. She watched friends fly off to the Florida Keys, some headed out West. She wanted bigger for her world too. My parents didn't see the purpose.

In Patience's absence, tensions mounted between my mother and me. I was the oldest in the house now, and that meant new rules. It also meant new scrutiny's, suspicions, and a lot of antagonistic attention. It was like my mother was the ultimate nemesis in the game of growing up, and once you had defeated the lower levels, she was the final brute to beat. Meanwhile, my friends seemed to be growing closer to their mothers with age. Every Monday, I was sulking through someone's riveting recount of their mommy-daughter weekend, complete with virgin mimosas and mani-pedis for the pair. My mother and I shared no such synergy.

I was afraid of my mother. That was by design. She didn't believe in being friends with your children, particularly when those children were young women. She felt like friendship fogged your perspective and made it impossible to parent your child in the proper direction. My mother had ample examples of mother-daughter friendships gone wrong, all of them ending in poverty and baby mama drama.

She made use of everyone's story but her own, and not knowing all that much about her, made closeness difficult. As children, the mommy we need is a caregiver, a nurturer, a nurse, etc. But as we age and our day-to-day demands no longer outweigh our social and psychological needs as young adults, the mommy we need is a mentor, a motivator, a mature sounding board. The relationship requires a deeper level of intimacy as we navigate our adolescence. The mother-daughter bond is supposed to mature as we do. As we become young women, the cradle-rocking mommy just won't cut it. Neither will the ruler with the iron fist. Young girls, especially, need to know womanhood that isn't wrecked by patriarchy's perspectives. They need to be free to explore their emotions, express their opinions, be wrong, be wild, fall, and find themselves, all without the world finding it offensive. Young girls need to know their mothers' stories because those stories give us a glimpse into the experiences that encapsulate our existence. No matter how ugly, how inappropriate, how embarrassing, how indicting, mothers owe daughters the intricate details of their origin. Else we let the world tell us who we are, who we've been, and who we're capable of being. My mother hoarded her story—all the while, denying her daughters the wisdom that accompanied her history. We learned our lessons the hard way while she lingered nearby, sometimes appearing satisfied with the sameness of our struggles. Perhaps her pain needed a companion.

Like that time we discovered Temi was in a relationship with a violent man, and that that violent man had been violent towards her. My mother remained unmoved, firm in her belief that Temi had turned her back to God by living in sin and having sex before marriage. It was what disobedience did; it killed your soul slowly. "The wages of sin are death," she would remind us, "and your sister is living in sin."

She kept her decade-long dance with domestic violence a secret, as she did all other aspects of her first marriage, not seeing how her secrecy led to our lack of awareness and overall unpreparedness. One by one, we took our turn with intimate partner trauma. A few of us circling the situation more than once. "I'll never understand why y'all have such poor taste in men," she would remark. It turns out we learned what we liked from her.

Our budding taste for traumatic relationships bloomed over time. Patience began perfecting her pallet during her first week on campus. A guy she met at freshman orientation invited her to a union party. She couldn't help but brag about it, casually mentioning her underclassman accomplishment to my father one evening over the phone. "It's not a party, Dad; it's more like a get together for the African students on campus," she explained. "It's cool meeting so many other Nigerians. Arah's gonna like it here," she assumed. I hadn't been accepted just yet, but I was fully committed to picking Pitt.

"Eh heh." My dad had a eureka. "You can take her with you this weekend. It will be good for her to be around our people, and she can see some of the campus. She will be joining you there by God's grace," he added optimistically.

Patience, on the other hand, was pissed. "Dad, Arah's in high school. She can't come to a college party." "But

Ifeoma, I thought it's not college party. Just a get-together." Patience was caught. Plus, you knew it was serious when my dad used your Igbo name. Patience was fully invested in the flimflam. She wasn't about to admit to clubbing one week into her freshman semester.

"It's okay, Dad. She can come," she caved. "That's good of you, Ife. It should feel good to include your sister."

"Yes, sir. It does," she lied. We were both good at that.

That weekend, my mom agreed to let me accompany Patience to the non-party. It was a Friday, which meant school came first. I could barely concentrate. This was my first college party, and I was damn excited about it. I was sixteen, which was the main thing that sucked about starting school so early. I felt I didn't get to enjoy any of the perks of being a typical teen. Most of the other seniors were eighteen years of age already or nearing their eighteenth birthday. There I was the same age as the sophomores.

Patience did not want to be at this college party with her sixteen-year-old sister; that much was clear. She didn't have to say it; it was obvious. She had carried her high school celebrity with her to college. I knew she didn't want to lose that. And what better way to blow your identity than by showing up at the first party of the semester with your teenage tomboy sister.

"Can't you throw on some eyeliner, at least?" Patience asked as she rushed past me to grab the gel beside the bathroom sink. "Which one is that?" I asked, holding two unrelated makeup products in my hands. To this day, don't ask me to identify the complete components of a beat face. Misogyny made sure makeup wasn't my thing. God forbid some random man see my freshly-made face and mistake me for a lady of the evening.

But I wasn't going to learn full glam in the bathroom of my sister's dorm room. And Patience lacked the patience to teach me anything I didn't already know. "Just throw on some lip gloss, then." That I could do; I applied a nice thick layer of my favorite corner store lip gloss, the kind that came with a roll applicator and was named after a fruit. Patience side-eyed the hell out of me the whole time. She was so embarrassed. And at the time, I thought it was more my age than anything else. I know now it was never that simple.

Eventually, a few friends joined Patience's pre-party function. All of them in their favorite late 90s fashions, what I like to call Cookout Couture. I was one to talk, standing there dressed as the leading lady in a Marilyn Manson video. None of us were making any best-dressed lists, that much I knew. While oddly onlooking the other girls as they preened and prepped themselves in the mirror dangling from the dormitory door, I overheard Patience debating with someone on her dorm room phone.

"I didn't know she was coming," she told the caller. "I can't; she's staying the night." I was all in the conversation, trying to decipher who didn't belong. *I hope these heifers got somewhere to sleep*, I snickered to myself, never once considering that the lingering lady in question was me.

It was almost time to head down to the union. The hallways hollered with the anticipation of a hundred first-year freshmen. The other girls finished fixing their tube tops, and I made sure my Chuck Taylor's were tied tight.

I was about to heel-toe my heart out; I hadn't been binge-watching Missy Elliot videos all week to be a wallflower.

As I gathered my things, Patience pulls me to the side.

"Hey, my friend said he can't get you in." "What do you mean? I thought I was using your ID."

"Yeah, well, I gave it to Allison," she said, pointing to her friend across the room.

"Well, what are we supposed to do?" I asked naively.

"Well," she paused awkwardly, "Arah, we're still going."

"How, if I can't get in?" It still hadn't hit me yet. "We" did not include me.

She attempted to explain it again. "So, we're already on the list. He just can't add you, you know, cause it's last minute." *This must've been some exclusive ass party.*

"Okay, I'll just ask Mom to come get me then."

"Why? You can still stay the night!"

What a weird and ineffective way to apologize. Besides, I wasn't too much a fan of her suggestion to stay. One of her roommates stayed behind, hoping to have some alone time with her boyfriend, which rarely happened in her quad.

"The 500 bus is still running," I reminded her. "I'll ask Mom to meet me downtown." It's always odd when I think back at how cavalier my mother was about us traveling alone, particularly on late nights. For her to have been so fixated on fearmongering us into celibacy, she sure seemed unconcerned about whom or what we would encounter out alone on the streets, you know, our actual safety. Not that we went looking for trouble, but it wasn't that hard to find in my hometown.

I agreed to stay with the promise that upon her return, Patience would take me to an all-night pizza place on campus, a hole in the wall called the "U." I slid my shoes off and climbed into a pod chair in the corner. Honestly, I was crushed. About an hour into an episode of *Law & Order*, there was a knock at the door. Pallavi, Patience's fourth roommate whom she'd known since high school, hopped off her top bunk and rushed to vet the visitor. It was her boyfriend. They hugged hard for a few minutes, letting the door slam behind them as they brushed back past me. *Yep. This was my queue to call it a night.* I gathered my belongings as the pair disappeared in Pallavi's pillows.

165

Alone, I hit the mean streets of Pitt's infamous college quad, a neighborhood known as Oakland. This is where four local universities melded into one main stretch of street. Students crowded every corner in-between classes, bumping shoulders and messenger bags as they ran from building to building. They draped cars in campus flags and covered their backs in the ancient alphabet. It was a different world than the one we knew. An exciting world, a much safer space than the one I was from, or so I assumed.

As I scaled the sidewalks, passing puking frat boys and homeless men with money cups, I thought how I couldn't wait to get to college. I could smell the freedom. It stank. It did what the fuck it wanted to do, and it didn't care who was caught watching. I wanted to know what that was like. To dance at a party without gawking at the clock. I felt like Cinderella, sometimes. Just that there was no secret soirée to attend, and no fickle fruit to assist in my escape.

I began the first leg of my journey, hopping on one of the many city buses that passed through Pitt's bustling campus. In the evenings, I knew to sit right behind the driver. You did this to avoid the creeps who frequented the corner seats at the back of the bus after dark. And then there was always the surprise piss left lingering by someone who couldn't be bothered to hold it any longer. But for as much as I hated having to catch the bus everywhere, especially in the winter, I appreciated the show. There was always something to see on a city bus, and tonight, there was a fight.

A verbal one, not with all the pushing and shoving. Two older women yelled back and forth about whose bags were taking up the bulk of the aisle. At one point, the argument turned personal. The bus driver watched through her rearview mirror, almost missing her turn into the city. She slammed the breaks, jolting everyone forward. Grocery bags came flying down the aisle. One of the women jumped from her seat to stop what she could.

"Sorry, y'all!" the driver yelled. Easing off the breaks before breezing by a few people standing at another corner stop. "Hey!" another rider yelled. "That's my stop!" She pointed as we passed it. "My bad. Lemme let you off at the next one." Drivers like her were the worst, just doing whatever they wanted to do.

"Imma hop off with her," I said, standing up. "Gotchu." She nodded into the mirror. We all hopped off together. The shared eye contact was a silent sigh of relief.

I thought about whether I'd tell my parents what I was doing strolling in the house after hours. I never told on Patience; it was a part of the code, but she was on thin ice with me. Sometimes it seemed she was mean just for the fuck of it. Embarrassed by me, embarrassed by all of us.

I took my time climbing the steep hill that dropped me off at my doorstep. Usually, I made it a point to haul ass. I had grown paranoid ever since three guys held up my dad halfway up the hill. I used to wait for him on the front porch to hike the hill after work. I could bet on the late bus to drop him off around 2:41 a.m. By 2:45 a.m., I was waiting patiently on the front porch furniture.

Somehow, I thought my being there kept him safe. But tonight, fear was the furthest thing from my mind.

I fumbled through my many keys to find the one that fit our front door. Before I could finish unlocking the double lock, someone on the other side began to assist.

"Hi, Dad," I said, assuming it was him. He rarely slept at night; his body had adjusted to working an overnight job.

"Adaeze!" he called out. "You're home so soon." We hugged tightly.

"Yes, Sir. I couldn't get into the party without an ID."

"Does Ifeoma not have so many IDs?" he asked, stunned.

"Her friend is using it." His eyes got wide. "You mean she gave the ID to her friend." "Yes, Sir."

"And left her junior sister to return home on the bus."

"Well, she didn't make me leave, but I didn't want to wait in her dorm."

"Hey! Chineke!" my dad exclaimed, tossing both arms around his head.

"Who is that!?" my mom called out from the stairwell.

"Arah is home," my dad called back.

"Hey, Mom."

"Hey, what's wrong?"

"Nothing's wrong, Mom. I couldn't get in." "Patience didn't know you couldn't get in before she invited you?"

"Mom, I don't know. It's not a big deal." "Well, call her," my mom hollered.

"She's at that party, Mom. She's not gonna answer."

"Call her anyway!" my dad hollered. How the hell this was turning towards me, I hadn't the slightest clue. But I did as I was told while my parents fussed back and forth in the background.

"No one answered," I said, hanging up the phone.

"Call her again!" my dad said. *And this is exactly why I keep secrets.* This time Pallavi answered the phone.

"Hello?" She sounded half asleep.

"Hey, Pallavi, it's Arah. I'm sorry to bother you so late. Is Patience in?"

"No, she hasn't gotten back yet. But I'll let her know you called."

"Ok, thanks," I said, quickly ending the call.

"I will call her first thing tomorrow morning," my Dad proclaimed, pissed.

"Ndo," he apologized in Igbo.

"It's okay, Dad," I said, slipping up the stairs.

The next morning, I was met by a barrage of missed calls. "Patience called for you," my mother mentioned after our morning mumble. I had no plans to call back. "Oh, okay, I'll call her later." Just then, my dad appeared from his prayer room. We greeted each other, briefly bantering for a moment. "I spoke to your sister," he began. "And I feel you should forgive her. I don't agree with her decision, but her reasoning is good." "Reasoning, what was the reason?" I said under my breath.

"Yes, it's not a good crowd for your young age," my dad said. I had no clue what cover story she told him, but I could tell it was convincing.

Before we could finish talking, the phone rang again. "Arah," my mother called for me. "It's your sister." I didn't see the point in speaking about it any further.

How many ways did she need to say she didn't want me around? "Go'an speak with your sister," my dad nudged. I begrudgingly grabbed the phone.

"Hello?"

"Hey," Patience replied.

"Mom said you wanted to speak to me?"

"Yeah, sorry about last night."

"It's cool," I replied. Completely disinterested in her clean up attempt.

"Do you wanna come to the twenty-one and under club with us on Friday?"

"I still don't have an ID," I said sarcastically.

"You can use mine."

"Okay, sure." I didn't believe her one bit. *This was some sick joke*, I told myself as she ran off the details on the other end. Hanging the phone with no intention of taking her sad ass sorry seriously. "How did it go?" my dad asked as if he already knew.

"It went fine, Dad. I'm gonna see her on Friday."

"That's good!" he celebrated. My mother seemed to be side eyeing the whole situation and probably trying to figure out how I planned to get there? Remember, Dorothy Jean was nobody's chauffeur.

All week I waited for Patience to pull the plug on our party plans. I made it a point not to get excited on purpose; I knew this was too good to be true. But Wednesday quietly came and went, Thursday did too. Before I knew it, Friday was at my door. I called Patience's dorm room, just to test the waters.

"Hey," I said, catching her on the first ring, "Am I still coming to Oakland today?"

"Hey! Yeah, my last class ends at 4:50 p.m., so you can come any time after that."

"Okay, cool." I was still sensing a setup. I just knew I was being bamboozled, but with no proof, I had to play along.

I got to the university quad around a quarter to eight. Patience came down to meet me in the lobby of her building. We hugged.

"Hey, Arah!"

"Hey," I said back. I followed her into the elevator. She had already begun her makeup. "Who else is coming?" I asked.

"Just Alison, Kristen, and Kemba."

"Have you met Kemba?"

"No, I don't think so."

The truth was, I wouldn't remember if I did; I was horrible with informal social introductions.

We hopped off the elevator on a different floor than the last time. The pre-party was moved from Patience's room because Pallavi's parents were on campus for a visit. We got to the door and pushed our way in.

"Kemba, this is my little sister, Arah."

"Oh, hey, Arah," Kemba called out from the kitchenette.

"Hey," I hollered back. I knew not to get too comfortable this time. I camped out in a corner on a beanbag, watching the other girls gallivant in front of the floor-length mirror.

When it was time to leave, I waited to hear my name called. Perhaps, Patience would request a second time that I wait behind. But my name never came. We walked halfway across campus and came upon a cluster of other clubgoers, all of them waiting for a ride on the university shuttle. We joined the others, who were seated all along the retaining wall. The shuttle rounded the corner, causing all of us to smash between the bus bench and the curb. This is happening, I considered for a minute. I couldn't believe I was headed to the club.

"Strip District" scrolled across the front of the bus in bright yellow letters. We made four more stops before making our way down a long stretch of a well-lit street. People lined the sidewalks on either side. There were clubs and bars on every corner. Horns honked as traffic stood still in the intersection. This was what I had waited for. It stank out here; the freedom, that is. I could smell it.

We neared the first stop on the Strip. Partygoers pushed their way to the front of the bus to make their exit.

"Hey," I said to Patience, "where's that extra ID you said you had for me?"

"I'll give it to you when we get off."

"Okay," I said, thinking nothing of it. We came to the second stop where more riders rose to their feet. Bars spilled into the streets with drunk college kids and young Pittsburgh partygoers. My head whipped left, right, and back and forth feverishly. I had lived in this city my whole life and never seen it so alive. This was happening. I was about to tear the club up.

We finally came to our stop on Smallman Street. As we crowded around the exit, I tapped Patience on the shoulder.

"Hey, don't forget, I need your ID."

"Yeah, I know," Patience replied. We shuffled down the bus stairs. The smell of Vladimir vodka filled the air.

It was disgusting in a delightful way.

We walked a block up the road, approaching a brightly lit building with a ramp for an entrance. "Patience!" a voice called out. Three girls came rushing our way from behind a parked Pontiac. Each of them reaching for someone to hug.

"Y'all just got down here?" one of them asked.

"Yeah," Patience replied. "Shuttle just dropped us off."

"Oh, this is your sister?" another inquired, pointing in my direction.

"Yeah, that's her," Patience replied. So much for an introduction.

We continued to move down the crowded sidewalk. Along the way, the girls stopped to greet people they knew. We came up under an iridescent sign on the side of a building, Club Yaga; the sign sang in bright orange. The other girls got in line. I nudged Patience; "Hey, where's the ID?"

"Oh yeah," she said, suddenly turning to Kemba.

"You have that ID I asked you to bring?"

"I thought I was using your ID!" I said frantically.

"You'll be fine, they don't care here," Kristen chimed in.

My heart stopped as I glanced down at the University of Pittsburgh ID Patience handed me. I looked nothing like the girl. Was this some sick joke? I pulled Patience by the arm. "This doesn't look like me, why can't I just use your ID? Look!" I shouted, holding the ID up to my face. One of the other girls giggled. "What the fuck!" I said, starting to feel sick to my stomach. "What happens if I can't get in?"

"I said you'll be fine," she flipped. "Just make sure you know the information in case they ask."

I looked down at the card, reading it repeatedly. If I was going to get into Club Yaga, I was going to have to make it stick.

"May 15, 1984. May 15, 1984."

As I recited the stranger's birthday, I could hear Alison doing the same.

"April 11, 1985. April 11, 1985."

I recognized the birthday; it belonged to Patience. I instantly realized that Alison was using the extra ID, the same one Patience promised to lend me. Here she was once again, leaving me ass out for a friend. I was furious. There was no way in hell I could pass for the person on this ID. I couldn't believe she would pull something like this in public. The last thing I wanted was to be the reason no one got to go to the club.

We inched closer to the door—my heart beating out of my chest. "Just be cool about it. It's not a big deal if you don't make it weird." Patience's friends sucked, and so did their advice. One by one, the bouncer took a flashlight to our IDs; another patted us down for weapons.

178

They lied when they said it wasn't serious, it looked damn serious to me.

Patience was up next. The first bouncer flicked his flashlight from his hand to her face and back.

"What's your name?" he asked, sounding it out in his head.

"Patience Ifeoma Iloabugichukwu."

"Perfect!" he smiled, passing her the ID. She moved to the left of the line, where bouncer number two searched her purse. I handed my fake ID to the first bouncer. I could hear my heart pounding in my head. He lifted his eyes above his glasses, then glanced back down at the ID. Then up at me again, then back down to the ID. "What's your name?" he asked.

"Brishelle Ruffin."

"Spell it."

"B-R-I-S-H..."

"Sweetie," he interrupted me, "I can tell you're under 21, but you gotta have a valid ID for me to let you in this nightclub. And there is no way this light-skinned lady is you. Sorry." He handed me back the useless piece of plastic. He probably almost felt bad for me. It was truly a pathetic sight.

I took my teary eyes and sunk to the side of the line. Other partygoers looked on in pity. It was a walk of shame if I'd ever seen one. Patience called me over from behind the black rope that separated the partygoers from the public.

"What happened?" she asked like a dumbass. "You know what happened! It didn't work."

"Wow, that's crazy! What are you about to do?" I almost couldn't speak. I just stared up at my sister. Why didn't she have any empathy for me?

"What am I about to do?"

"Yeah, I can't ask them to leave now that they're already in," she said seriously.

"Well, can I use your buspass?" At this point, I was just trying to get out of there before the waterworks began. I didn't care that she hated me. I didn't care that I embarrassed her. I didn't care about the club or hanging with kids in college. I was cold and alone; I wanted to go home.

She stared back blankly. "I can give you bus fare, but I need my bus pass." She handed me a dollar bill and some change before disappearing into the denseness. A piece of me struggled to understand what happened, although I knew better than to get my hopes up with Patience. But for whatever reason, I wanted her to miss the regard we once had for one another. We didn't always exist in this perpetually, painful space.

I wasn't fully familiar with the Strip District. I had never been this deep into the area, especially not at night. As I approached a busy intersection, I spotted a friend from school. "Christy!" I called out. Her face dropped as she spotted me. "What the hell are you doing here, Arah?" she asked as we hugged.

"About to go home," I huffed.

"My sister just played me." My friends knew how strict my mother was, so it was a big deal that I was even out at that hour.

"What do you mean she played you?"

"She promised me I could use her ID then gave it to someone else at the door."

"Yeah, that's messed up," Christy said. "You can come with me if you want to. My friend has a school ID you can use, and you could easily pass for her." She motioned for her friend to join us near the streetlight, offering her a brief rundown of the situation.

"Damn. That's messed up," she said in consolation. "I'm sorry she did that to you. Yeah, they do not play around here. Here!" She passed me her school ID. "You could easily pass for me. Christy can go in between us." *This was about to happen; after all.* Suddenly, I stopped. "I have to ask my mom."

Christy pulled out her cell phone. "Here, just call her. Tell her I'll drop you off after we leave." It was cute that she thought it was that simple. Dorothy was a little more difficult than that. The first try went to voicemail. Call her back, Christy nudged.

"She gonna be mad," I said, hittingthe call button a second time. My mother picked up on the first ring.

"Hello?"

"Mom, it's me."

"Whose phone are you calling me from?"

"Christy, from school."

"Hi, Mom!" Christy attempted to butter her up from the background.

"Where's Patience?"

"I don't know."

"What do you mean, you don't know?"

"She left me standing outside the club because I couldn't get in."

"So, how did you end up with Christy?"

"I ran into her on my way to the bus stop to come home."

"Is she bringing you home?"

"Well, she said I could come with her and her friend to another club, and they would drop me off afterward."

"Absolutely not, come home!"

"But Mom, why not? You know Christy's parents. You can even call her mom if you want to."

Christy nodded in confirmation.

"I'm not calling nobody this late, bring your tail home."

"Mom, I never get to go anywhere. You said I could go out tonight."

"I said with your sister! Not to run off with your little friends."

"But Patience ran off with hers!"

"Bring your behind home, now!

my mother said, slamming the phone.

"I'm sorry, Arah." Christy hugged me. "I can still take you home."

"No, go ahead," I said, backing away. I needed the quiet time for a few reasons, but mainly for complaining and crying. As we said our goodbyes, I sulked down the street towards my bus stop, tears tumbling down the sides of my face. I hated it here. I hated all of it. Why did I have to watch from the wings while everyone enjoyed their teens?

It took me over twenty minutes to reach where I waited for the bus. As I sat down on the bench, a black truck pulled up beside me. The window slowly rolled down as I squinted to see who was behind the wheel. "Aye, Arah," a voice called out. "Remember me?" It was Cori, an old acquaintance from summer camp. "Boy, you scared me."

"My bad, I mean no harm. How you been, though? You out pretty late tonight."

"Yeah, I know."

Not wanting to go into too much detail, I told him I was headed home from a friend's place.

"Your friend ain't got no car," he joked.

184

"No, plus freshman can't have cars on campus."

"You can ride with me. Where you stay? Still up off Perrysville?"

"Ahh, yeah, but you don't have to do that. The bus should be here soon."

"I can't let you wait here by yourself. You know how downtown gets. C'mon now," he said as he unlocked the passenger door.

"Hurry up before this cop pulls up behind me."

"I'm good, Cori. Go 'head." I laughed nervously.

"I'm not playing, girl, get in. Won't even take ten minutes to get there." He smiled. We stared across the street at each other.

"We wasting time out here," he said.

"I'm good, Cori. Thank you."

"So, I'm just out here looking dumb then, huh? I'm tryna be nice and offer you a ride. You seriously not gone take it?" We stared again, momentarily. He unbuckled his seat belt, leaning across the seat and shoving the passenger door open.

"C'mon Arah," he said sternly. "We wasting time out here."

CHAPTER 10

CHRISTINA AGUILERA

A JOURNAL ENTRY ON SEXUAL ASSAULT

One of the most important things a mother can teach her young daughter is her right to say, "No." And I mean to anything, to compliments, casual conversation, date night invitations, meetup locations, help, hugs, clothing suggestions, and mood corrections. No is the most important word a girl can learn. Mothers teach their daughters that their bodies are deserving of respect and space, but only when they believe the same about themselves. My mother saw things differently, which unfortunately meant I was never armed with the word "No."

I can't blame my mother for struggling to understand healthy boundaries, being somewhat confused about consent. I can't say it was something I heard or saw anywhere—quite the contrary, to be honest. Obligatory touch was a regular topic. "We hug around here," was a typical retort to requests for personal space. I remember watching while my mother mulled over old church drama, gossiping in the middle of the grocery store with women she didn't even like. But rude was not a right we possessed. If someone wanted your time and attention, you gave it, even if reluctantly. I was learning to be inauthentic in the name of neighborliness. Our culture was warm and welcoming; my mother would remind me, even when doing so, drove you insane.

When we entertained guests, almost weekly, I was constantly reminded of just how exposed I was. I hated our infamous house parties; thirty to forty West Africans packed from the kitchen to the front porch. "Come and hug me, you know I'm your uncle na," the strange men would say. Of course, we knew to oblige their requests. Either that or catch hell. "This is our culture," my dad would remind us. And there was no arguing with that. If only my parents knew how much their cultures had in common. Conclusion: there was no personal space more important than the community's closeness, so personal aversions served no purpose.

Weekend after weekend, I watched my mother hug men she hated and cater to characters she found offensive. It was a woman's duty to do what she did. Ignore her boundaries and prioritize the experience of others. God forbid she appear to be an angry Black woman. Somewhere between obligation and offense, she'd be expected to find a balance. Her daughters inherited her dutifulness.

As a young Black girl, you weren't supposed to have boundaries. Why? Simple: Boundaries hurt men's feelings. If a boy pushed you on the playground, you were to tell yourself that he liked you. And if he picked on you in class, you were to say to yourself; he envied your intelligence. And if he pulled your pigtails, you were to tell yourself that he was in awe of your attractiveness. Under no circumstances were you to ask him to stop. You didn't know his intent. He was owed the benefit of benevolence. That was a young woman's duty.

To defend the questionable intent of men. After all, we already knew women weren't to be trusted. Somewhere between learning to ignore our boundaries and coddling cultural toxicity, they expected us to keep ourselves safe, virtuous, and secure. No one told us how. Likely because it's impossible to protect yourself without making it a priority. Instead, they sent us out into the world bound by patriarchy's playbook, all the while expecting us to win a game with rules designed to deny us even the smallest victory. It was a wager we couldn't win.

I cautiously climbed inside Cori's car. "Damn. Can I get a hug?" I obliged his request. I sat with my hands tucked between my legs, quietly instructing him on which left turn to take to cross the bridge to my side of town. "I know another way," he said, rushing through red lights. We engaged in small talk for a while, when I noticed we were driving in the opposite direction. "My house is the other way," I reminded him. He claimed he hadn't forgotten. "I know where you stay; I just need to make a stop." *Mom is going to kill me*; I kept telling myself. Even at that moment, I lacked the awareness to

190

see how this situation was far more dangerous than Dorothy's blows might have been.

We rode quietly for another fifteen minutes, making our way to a neighborhood known as Garfield. Cori pulled up to what looked like an abandoned storefront.

"You tryna come in?"

"I can wait in the car."

"Aight," he said as he exited. "Nah, matter fact, I don't want you waiting here by yourself, come in. It'll be real quick." I didn't say no. I didn't know how to. I climbed out of the car, following Cori to the back of the building. He pushed the door open, allowing me to enter ahead of him.

"You can wait right there," he said, pointing to a blanket sprawled out on the floor.

"On the floor?"

"Why, you too bougie to sit on the floor?" I didn't answer. I walked over to where the blanket was laid out, opting instead to lean against the wall.

For what seemed like forever, Cori fumbled around in an office cabinet.

"You got a boyfriend," he asked.

"Yeah," I lied nervously.

"No, you don't," he laughed. "At camp, you couldn't even look at a boy, now all of a sudden you gotta boyfriend?"

"Yep," I lied again.

"How old are you anyway, seventeen?"

"Sixteen."

"Oh, okay, you only two years younger than me. And you pretty."

I didn't respond. I couldn't. I didn't know where I was or how I was getting home. Things were getting weirder, and I blamed myself for whatever was about to happen. I should have gotten on the bus; I shouldn't have gone to Pitt, to begin with. No matter what happened to me, if I survived the ordeal, Dorothy was just going to kill me anyway.

"You like music?" he asked.

"Sometimes."

He grabbed a portable stereo from underneath the metal desk attached to the filing cabinet and turned on the local radio station. Christina Aguilera screamed through the speakers. "You like Christina Aguilera?" he asked.

"She scream too much for me." I didn't reply again. "Why you all the way over there? I'm 'bout to come over there with you." He made his way to the blanketed area where he'd sent me to sit. I could feel the hair on my arms rising as he made his way across the room. "You grew up since our summer camp days," he said. "Hair got all long; you ain't used to wear it straight like this." He reached out to touch my hair. I tilted my head away from his hand. "Damn! I'm being nice to you!" he yelled. "You acting like you don't even know me."

I didn't. Sure, we attended the same summer camp, but Cori and I were never close. I knew him in passing the same way I did many other attendees. Not only was he a grade above me, but we also didn't run in the same circles. "I was just trying to get home," I whispered. "And imma take ya ass home, damn! Yo, you fuckin' ungrateful!" he said, inching closer. "Come here." He gripped me by my bicep. I lifted my arm to allow it, refusing to move the rest of my body. "Come here!" he said, raising his voice. This time he tugged me by my arm. I had no clue how I was getting out of here. As the moments passed, it appeared less and less likely.

"My mom is waiting for me."

"And I said imma take you home," Cori huffed again. "You wasn't in a rush at the bus stop." He lifted his hand to my hair. I didn't know what to do. Honestly, we don't prepare young women to escape sexually aggressive situations. We put the burden of avoidance on young women while simultaneously raising young men to believe that sex is a social achievement, a service even.

Cori's aggressive character is what makes this story particularly heinous, but in his way of thinking, he's hardly alone. He felt that I owed him a debt, and repayment was on his terms. His repeated reminders of how he'd treated me with kindness were an indication that he believed he'd exceeded the standard for how he had to treat a young Black woman. He was kind enough to offer me a ride. He coerced me to take it, so what? I owed him for it. I had no right to say no.

In a way, I agreed with him that I was without right. From as early as I could remember, I was at the whim of men's affection. There was no right way to tell a man he was wrong. Instead, we smiled through unwanted hugs and uncomfortable back rubs, whispering in secret spaces, which ones to avoid.

We had no right to say, "No." Only a little girl with no home training would test an adult that way. "If Uncle' Such N Such' does anything, you let me know." That's how it was handled. And quite a few of them knew already. The others didn't want to.

"Why you acting scared?" Cori ran his hands through my hair. "I'm being nice to you, ain't I?" he said a second time. He was proud of himself.

"Sit down!" he said in a stern voice. Squatting to the floor and patting it two or three times.

"I wanna stand. Why can't I stand?"

He grabbed my ankle and yanked it forward, causing me to stumble backward, landing on my hands.

"I'm tryna be nice to you, Arah. Sit up!"

This time I listened.

"You a virgin?" Cori inquired.

"Yeah." I wanted to keep it that way.

I used my feet to force my body back against the wall, hugging my knees to my chest. Cori moved directly next to me. I knew I was stuck.

"Can I call my mom?"

"I don't have no cell phone. You bout to see her anyway though."

"Whe-?"

He leaned in and kissed me before I could finish.

"When?" I finished anyway.

He put his hand on my knee.

"Relax. Imma take you home in a little while."

I closed my eyes and began to cry. How did I end up here with a guy I hardly knew, on the floor of a gutted storefront? Had I not tried to party with Patience, had I just stayed away from Pitt, none of this would ever have happened. I just had to stop and talk to Christy, didn't I? I knew my mom would say no. Why waste time?

Time was what got me into this trouble to begin with. I blamed myself. I shouldn't have been out so late alone. And look at what I was wearing. Could I blame the guy? What did I expect him to expect from me, if not fun?

He crawled down by my feet, forcing them apart with his knees.

"You a virgin for real? You know we can tell."

Grabbing me by both of my ankles, he yanked my feet out from under me. My back hit the floor. I tried to sit up again, but he shoved me down, pinning me to the floor with his forearm.

"Why you playing?"

He tugged at my skirt button. Our hands tussled over the top of it.

"Please stop!" I said, still struggling with his hands.

"Stop what?"

"Please stop!"

"Stop what?" he asked again.

Now we were engaged in a full-on tug of war over the clothing wrapped around my waist. I could see him becoming more frustrated as our fingers locked in a fight. He grabbed my hand and bent it backward. I let out a groan, gripping his arm to try and make him release me. He bent back further.

"Let go!" I cried.

"Oh, you want me to be nice to you again?" He continued to press on my palm. His expression switched from serious to smiling. "Apologize!" He squeezed my hand even harder. "Say sorry!" he instructed me, sternly.

"I apologize! I'm sorry!"

"You sorry? You sure?"

I nodded my head in response, clutching my hand as he released his grip.

I couldn't believe this was happening to me. I wasn't some fast ass girl. I didn't go to parties. I rarely ever hung out with friends. I didn't date or have sex of any kind. By other mothers' standards, I was a decent daughter. My mother warned me of the wages of sin. And ironically, this felt a lot like death.

I laid there silently as Cori went back to unbuttoning my skirt. He fumbled around frantically for a few minutes, before becoming frustrated again. He began pushing my skirt up from the bottom, folding it upwards around my waist. My fingers browsed the blanket fibers like braille. His voice faded in and out as my mind wandered away, trying desperately to stay distant. He pulled my underwear down around my ankles. The jerk jolted me back to reality. I stared into the ceiling so hard I felt for a moment I could bring it down. I tried. No luck.

Cori climbed on top of me. The pungent perfume of menthol muffled my breathing. I wept without making a sound, staring into the dim ceiling light. Tears filled my ears. I became convinced that I could hear the hum of the ocean. I tried drowning myself in the currents of my imagination, holding my breath, and hoping to hide all remaining signs of life. He had already ignored so many.

Cori began trying to force himself inside of me. I squeezed everything, from my eyelids to my toes. It felt like fire. Like my skin was being split. He pushed for what felt like forever. I couldn't tell if he was done or not. The pain was inexplicable. "You a virgin for real, huh?" He said before forcing a finger inside of me. The pain gave my suffering sound, and it upset him.

"Seriously?" he asked sarcastically. "You ain't even get fucked for real?" He pushed his hand in and out of me. "I gotta loosen you up first." He reached behind my head, retrieving a rusted torque wrench. "Imma go slow," he forewarned me. Right before shoving the rusted wrench inside my vagina. I had cried for so long that the back of my hair had become wet from the water. I traced the ceiling tiles to pass the time. Once again, it was the time that had betrayed me.

I became fixated on what my parents would say when they found out. It felt like we'd been here for hours. All these years my mother spent warning me about the importance of purity, my virginity, my virtue, and here it was, lost in a matter of minutes. It was what made me valuable and rendered me worthy in terms of my womanhood. "No man wants to be with somebody that's been ran all through," my mother often warned. "It's unbecoming of a young woman to be with this guy and that." What kind of woman did this make me?

"What the fuck, you on your period?!" Cori yelled. I wasn't. I had never even had a monthly cycle. He knew nothing about a woman's body; nothing about the female anatomy he had spent the last hour violating. "Where all this come from then?" he said as he held the bloody torque wrench up to my face. I rolled over on my side, gripping my abdomen in agony. "And you got blood on my blanket too! Man. Get dressed!" He stood up from his knees, shoving his limp penis back inside his boxer shorts. "Get dressed!"

I reached for my ripped skirt, pulling it back down below my bottom. I thought if I moved with too much enthusiasm, he might change his mind. I felt filthy. I pushed myself up with my palms, hugging my knees, horrified at what had just happened. Cori went back to rummaging through an old desk, undeterred. I didn't dare ask him about home again. My only concern now was leaving alive.

And at the same time, I felt reluctant to leave. So much of a young girl is predicated on what she believes about herself. And when culture is corrupted under the pressures of patriarchy, young girls are made to believe whatever misogyny maintains about them. In my case, the rules of misogyny were clear. It was a young woman's ability to remain righteous that rendered her worthy. As it stood, I was no longer worthy.

The letdown was layered. Cori wasn't just a coward; there was much more to his character than just repressed sexual aggression. He was a high school dropout, had been in and out of juvenile detention centers, and by all accounts, was stuck in the streets. I knew never to get caught up with a guy like Cori. I wasn't a girl after the fast life. That stress just wasn't for me, which made my dilemma that much more devastating. In my mind, I had done just about everything I could to avoid this. I hadn't gone looking for a guy like Cori, so why had he come looking for me?

As a child, you're taught that there are good girls and bad girls, and good guys and bad guys, and on either side, a spectrum from subtle to severe. The good girls and the good guys do good things in the world, the bad girls and guys do the same. Good guys attract good girls; good girls attract good guys, and again, bad girls and guys repeat the pattern.

And this worldview is reinforced by our fables and fairy tales where the good guy rescues the good girl, pledging to love her forevermore. "Be the good girl" is what it says to you. "Be the good girl and get the good guy," is what it speaks to your subconscious.

It can take a lifetime to learn that the good girl milestone is a myth. There is no soft enough or strong enough, silly enough or serious enough, thin enough or thick enough to appease patriarchy's standards for a worthy woman. That level of untouchable doesn't exist— misogyny mars even the most moral of us. There is no pardon for purity within the system of patriarchy, which means I could have fallen victim in any version of my outfit, or at any time of the day.

Society would have us believe that we avoid violence through vigilance, but reality doesn't reflect that. Society would have us believe that men were more motivated by physical and visual stimulation than their naturally cerebral sisters. Science doesn't support that. Society would have us believe that an otherwise well-meaning man can be moved to immorality just by what a woman wears, but our lived experiences do not echo that.

Sexual assault affects women in short skirts just as much as it affects women in sweaters. Exotic dancers fall victim to sexual violence, just like Sunday school teachers do. Life teaches us that none of us are exempt if we all aren't exempt. The line is simply too thin to tow. At any given time, we walk a fine line between human and whore, running the risk of being caught with questionable character. And the wages of our sin are whatever men make them.

CHAPTER 11

MOMMA'S BOYS

A JOURNAL ENTRY ON SEXISM

After a while, the stress of the situation took its toll. I passed out. I woke up to Cori kicking my leg. "Get up. Time to go," he said. It took me a moment to realize it was now light outside. I may have survived the evening, but I didn't know what the day had in store. My mother was going to kill me. How could I explain to anyone what I'd just gone through? No one, especially not my mother, would believe that I'd been kidnapped and held against my will in an abandoned storefront all night. My clothes were dirty and blood-stained. My hair was disheveled. There was no lying my way out of this. I hated that I felt like I had to.

The drive home was painfully quiet. "You gone tell your parents what we did last night?" Cori asked, assaulting the silence. I didn't even address his gaslighting language. "No," I said—the audacity of him to imply that what happened was at my behest. I just wanted to get home without being hurt any further. I avoided the urge to address his wordplay. What good would it have done anyway?

"You gone give me your number?"

"I don't have a phone."

"You got a house phone."

"I'm not allowed to talk on the house phone." "Man whatever, fuck you then!" The silence settled in again.

Cori barely came to a complete stop before I rolled out of the passenger door. Car tires screeched as he sped off, making an unnecessarily dramatic escape. I hobbled up my parents' hill. My body didn't feel like my own. I had no clue how I would explain the events of the last twenty-four hours, but I desperately needed to lie down, at least I intended to.

I reached for my door key as I got to the top of my parents' stairs. The door flew open. "Where have you been?!" my mother yelled, swinging the screen door open.

"I don't know," I responded honestly.

"What you mean, you don't know?!" I brushed past my mother and attempted to head up the stairs.

"Excuse me!" she yelled. "Arah, I'm talking to you!"

"Mom, I need to lie down." I continued up the stairs. I heard her footsteps following behind me. So much for that nap. "Won't be no naps in this house today. Gia! Go grab my belt." Gia did as she was told.

I didn't even care. I was completely out of it, tired of being told what and what not to do. I climbed into bed in my dirty bloody clothes. My mother burst into the room.

"What is the matter with you? You don't hear me talking to you?"

"Mom, I just need to lie down. Please."

"No, you don't. What you need to do is tell me where the hell you been since yesterday."

"I don't know, Mom. I don't know where I was."

"Why is that? You were supposed to be on your way home from Pitt."

"I was."

"And?" she quizzed while squeezing the belt between her fingers.

"Some guy I knew offered me a ride." My mother started swinging the belt. I barely flinched. My body was so tired. I rolled onto my side to block some of the blows. Suddenly my mother stopped swinging.

"What's all this stuff on the bottom of your skirt? Blood?!"

I didn't answer. I was too ashamed.

"So, that's what you were out doing last night?!" The beating started again.

"I didn't want to!" I yelled back.

"So, somebody raped you. That's what you saying?"

I didn't answer. I didn't even know for sure what rape was. We'd been taught to keep an eye on the crackhead around the corner and the bums on the block when it was our day-to-day acquaintances who meant us the most harm. She stopped swinging again.

"You saying you were raped?"

"I think so."

"By who?"

"A guy I knew from camp."

"So, you had sex with him?"

I didn't understand the line of questioning.

"Mom, I said 'No.'"

"And…"

"And he did it anyway."

"See what happens when you don't listen to your parents?! You should've come straight home like I told you to."

"I tried, Mom."

"You obviously didn't try hard enough. Wait until your father finds out you're out here having sex. He is going to be sick."

I exploded into tears. I hated hearing how disappointed my father would be in me. Especially over something I had no control over.

"All this over some little boy. I hope it was worth it."

My mother stormed out of my room and slammed the door. I cried myself to sleep. It was the best rest I'd gotten in days.

I woke the next day wishing I could just die already. My mother had already let my dad in on my little situation. He called me outside where he'd been smoking

208

a cigarette and invited me to sit so that we could talk. I explained to my father what happened. My considerations at that moment were for him and his feelings, not for myself and my own. I attempted to omit the most disturbing details of my evening to spare him the disgust. My father cried beside me, and I cried too.

Then he apologized, although he struggled to offer much more condolence than that. He lit another cigarette. "I pray God never bless that boy to bring any child into this world." He puffed. "God will surely deal with him."

My dad was noticeably uncomfortable. I was too. I knew things would be different between us. No matter how much I tried to pretend. His little girl was gone. My whole life, he'd reminded me of the importance of my purity. He'd emphasized the value it had in the mating marketplace and the religious realm. Despite having empathy for me as his daughter, being a son of sexism meant he also felt quite a bit of disappointment. After all, patriarchy said my body was my burden to carry.

The question wasn't, "Why had the young man attacked me?" It was, "Why hadn't I done more to stop him?"

"It is well." My father consoled me some more. "Don't feel bad about it. It is well." We sat shoulder to shoulder. "You see now why your mama wanted sons." He burst into laughter. I laughed with him. My father always tried to turn a dark situation into a humorous one. Keyword: Tried.

We all knew my mother wished she'd only had sons. She audaciously told us often. She believed that raising girls was automatically a much more challenging task, given the greater risks, a job that required a firm hand, dedication, and a willingness to be the bad guy, a challenge my mother willingly accepted. But with her sons, she took a much gentler approach. Something raising sons would call for often.

My mother, like many mothers, was a sexist. Perhaps, she still is. Something I no longer fault her for. She loved all her children equally but openly practiced preferential treatment when it came to my brothers— something she denies to this day. But my father wasn't being funny; everyone knew of my mother's invisible inclination. Her behavior didn't half hide it either.

Maternal favoritism, a term used to describe a mother who displays preferential treatment towards one child over another, can take many forms: more privileges, fewer restrictions, more attention, less discipline, more affection, less abuse, more support, and less criticism. No matter the packaging, the poison stings the same. Every living example of maternal favoritism differs in her delivery, each mother guilty of her prejudices.

For some mothers, it's a matter of resemblance or likeness of the favorite child to a loved one or relative, living or deceased. For other mothers, it's a matter of preference in physical appearance. In many Black households, this is commonly caused by internalized anti-blackness and the self-defeating belief systems that uphold it, such as colorism, texturism, and featurism.

Sometimes, maternal favoritism is more perception than practice. When a child in the family has health challenges or special academic or intellectual needs that require more parental attention, siblings can grow up feeling unattended to or even ignored. But for many mothers, dare I say most, it's a gender elevation; an unconsciously slanted perception towards one sex over the other.

Gender bias is what it's called. For girls, it begins in the womb. We define it as a form of prejudice or discrimination based on a person's sexual identity alone. In some cultures, the partiality is more pronounced. Say, for example, in India, wherein 1990, the government was forced to pass legislation to combat standard practices like female infanticide and the selective abortion of female fetuses. Or in China, where laws against gender discrimination are neither accepted nor acknowledged, job qualifications often include things like height, body type, age, social status, demeanor, preferred phenotype, complexion, hair color, and other physical requirements. But these qualifications are almost exclusively for jobs considered to be more female-friendly, like computer programmer motivator. The only thing more concerning than the casual way societies worldwide practice patriarchy, or the systemic and social subjugation of women and girls, are the ridiculous reasons why.

I remember how excited my father was when my baby brother was born; you would've thought it was his first child. Growing up the daughter of a Nigerian immigrant meant a lot of things. It meant no eating or grabbing things with your left hand. It meant always remembering to greet your elders, calling every unfamiliar man and woman, "auntie" and "uncle." It also meant focusing on your studies and excelling in your academics, minding your senior siblings always. But most of all, it meant that my sisters and I were liabilities to my father. My brother, on the other hand, was a legacy. At my baby brother's naming ceremony, there was food and drink, dancers, chiefs, and masquerade costumes everywhere. I'd never seen my father so unreserved. He carried my brother around in his arms, smiling from ear to ear as guests placed their hands on his tiny head to offer their blessing. I watched from the porch stairs with my sisters; all dolled up for the occasion. I'm not gonna lie; we were peeved. In our house, holidays and special occasions revolved around Dad's seven-day prayer schedule. In all my years, I hadn't seen anything as essential to my dad as his morning mass. What was it about this kid, out of all my father's children, that warranted so much jubilee? Later that evening, we asked my dad why none of his daughters got naming ceremonies; none, not even the firstborn. He explained that although we were all gifts from God, my brother fulfilled both biblical and cultural prophecy. Not to mention, my brother would carry on our last name long after finding a wife, we would belong to our future husbands. In other words, it was his Igbo obligation, his religious responsibility to have a son, for the preservation of our family legacy, both back home and here in America. Something his daughters could not do.

We watched our mother be soft and sweet with our baby brother, Uche, a luxury we were yet to earn through the years. The world would already be too tough on him, so she took it upon herself to be the lamb in his life.

While my brother enjoyed extended adolescence, dodging accountability in every stage of his development, we were being held to a barometer of maturity that muted our girlhood. The time for dolls and mommy-daughter tea parties was brief. By middle school, we'd shifted our sights to adulthood, and we had a lot of preparation to do.

214

We had no choice but to be strong Black women in the works. We spent our youth practicing womanhood and refining independence: summer jobs, rigorous academic curriculums, added household responsibilities, many of them Uche's, a bill here and there, child-rearing responsibilities. We were being prepared for adulthood, right down to taking care of the men in our lives. There was no doubt about that. Over time, the nurturing, gentle approach that accompanied my mother's motherhood in our infancy was no more. Now, we gained acceptance in her home the same way we gained it globally by proving we were worth it.

Why? Because womanhood is burdensome. At least that's what patriarchy tells us. My mother bought into that. She saw caring for her sons as an act of selflessness; her daughters, she considered them to be indebted.

We're programmed to see our unborn daughters as threats to our beauty and our bodies from pregnancy, operating from a deficit before they're born. It makes you wonder how many of us were formed in the framework of our mother's unconscious ill will towards womanhood and all that birthing another woman entailed. When the bias is quiet, it's harder to hear. Meaning it's easier to be complicit in a discriminatory diatribe when its impact and intent are invisible. It's what we're not saying with our subtle submissiveness that says a lot. The evasiveness of our bias is what makes it so brutal. Before we know it, we're already on board with treating womanhood like a wound.

Much like racism requires a collective devaluation of the oppressed party, sexism does much of the same. It's not enough to argue that patriarchy persists because boys and men hold substantially more significant value. We must simultaneously become convinced that girls and women do not. The slander doesn't stop in the belly. Every stage in a young girl's development is met with a list of things to look out for. Girls are presumed to be temperamental, moody, unappreciative, and sneaky. And while we hear and internalize these falsities about ourselves, we believe them about one another, whether it is our intent or not. My mother loved her daughters; she just never learned how to like us. In a world where women and girls are taught to see each other as virtue-less, perpetually petty threats to one another's standing in

216

society; it's tough not to form relationships with other women that aren't based on competition and conflict. Mother-daughter relationships are not exempt.

And all this is heightened for young girls and women who are members of marginalized communities like the Black community. If we carry these negative characterizations in our subconscious, it's not surprising that we unconsciously apply them whenever we see an opportunity. And there's always an opportunity to make another woman look bad, especially when that woman is your daughter.

It's about proximity, not the intent. We tend to hurt those closest to us. That's what makes gender bias a double-edged sword. It works both with and against us. We think it shapes our view of the world, but it really alters our lens, and that lens reconstructs our reflection just as much as it poisons our perspective. If we believe women are inherently bad, we believe the same about ourselves, whether knowingly or unknowingly. And when we raise our daughters, who are often reflections of ourselves, we subject them to the same abuse that we feel we deserve. If we attribute sexuality with salaciousness, we'll punish our daughters for being sexual beings. If we liken weakness with femininity, we'll condemn our daughters for embracing their natural feminine essence. If we believe that respect is based on behavior, we'll excuse abuse when it reinforces our version of virtue. It's hard to build a healthy relationship with any young woman when you don't think highly of women, particularly the woman you are. It's equally challenging for someone to build a healthy relationship with you.

My mother wasn't intentionally emotionally closed off from her daughters. Fundamentally, she viewed women with distrust, which made vulnerability feel like venom. My mother wasn't secretive and suspicious of her daughters because it was enjoyable, but because she believed that women, regardless of their good intentions, were almost always looking out for their own best interests, which made honesty and openness impractical. My mother struggled with being empathetic about my assault because she'd been conditioned to find me at fault, an action key to the preservation of patriarchy. There is no flip switch that snaps us out of our bias or breaks decades of conditioning. If we are biased before motherhood, we will view motherhood through those biases. Being related to a woman doesn't nullify the negative views we hold about women in general. That's the thing about bias; before we know it, we've already been applied.

There's nothing volatile about our periods. The judgmental stares of both men and women shouldn't batter our blossoming bodies. We become the cold, cruel world we once navigated ourselves as young women, feeling vindicated as we watch our daughters navigate nearly identical obstacles with limited guidance. We tell ourselves we're making our daughters tougher. The world wouldn't understand; we're brewing strong Black women. But when we haven't healed from the pain of our bias towards ourselves, we delight in how those biases debilitate others. Once again, our daughters are not exempt from that.

My mother loved me. I have no doubt that she did, and still does. But she could have loved me without limitations had society not convinced her that we were undeserving.

CHAPTER 12

DATE MY DAD

A JOURNAL ENTRY ON DATING

They say if you marry a man like your father, you become a woman like your mother. Whoever "They" are, they have never been more right. There is a benefit to the indirect perspective you have as a daughter. It keeps you guarded against the gritty details of who your dad is as a man. I always thought the world of my dad, and I still do. My love obsession with him began when I was just a little girl. He would be the first man I would fall in love with. And he could do no wrong; I wouldn't even consider it. We loved each other eagerly. At times, my mother looked on in envy. I was proud of my father and felt very protective of him. His coming to America had not been kind.

And although my father was my favorite guy, he was far from perfect. His human hierarchy went a little something like this; Heavenly Father; then friends; and finally, family. Meaning we were last in line for his attention, although we never felt neglected entirely. He was there for early morning storytelling, late-night Jerry Springer reruns, bus rides around the city, and birthday celebration songs, far more than my friends could say about their dads.

My most unforgettable memories are moments shared with him. Dancing around the dining room as King Sunny Ade poured from the speakers, laughing that ridiculously loud laugh of his. I adored that laugh so much.

My father was a fan of fatherhood, never becoming annoyed by how annoying we were, always embracing a gentler tone, and taking the time to explain his adult decisions. In his decorated diction, he confessed his love for us daily. Never missing an opportunity to tell us just how highly he thought of us, whether we agreed or not.

He fathered us well, and this was well known. "I wish I had your dad," my friends doted with envy. He loved us in a way that the world could see and wouldn't apologize for that. I told myself in the future; I would marry a man like my father. Someone who loved me like it was the law. Someone kind, gentle, understanding, and supportive. All the accolades I attributed to my father, I hoped I would find in him. And as luck would have it, I did. Well, sort of.

At 21, I met a man. His name was Adeyinka. Beautiful, brown-skinned, bow-legged. Physically, he checked every box. He worked at a West African nightclub, a friend and I used to frequent. We spotted him a time or two until finally, a mutual friend made the introduction. He was somewhat shy, appeared to be loved by just about everyone in attendance. We exchanged numbers and began to talk from time to time. Like my father, he was born and raised back in Nigeria, a Yoruba boy, to be exact. The sweet sound of his accent felt so familiar to me: his gentle demeanor, a carbon copy of my father's.

The more we spent time with one another, the closer together we grew. It was a sense of respect we shared for each other. There was never any pressure or any unrealistic expectations. Adeyinka allowed me to be myself and praised me for my ability to do just that. Never quick to anger, always willing to explain. Everything I adored about my father as a daughter, I saw in him. It was a beautiful sight to behold.

But the similarities didn't stop there. Yinka, as I would come to call him, had his flaws too. Just like my father, he had his human hierarchy. First friends, then fun, then family. But the club had no competition. Not only was it his livelihood, but it was also where he went to long for his life back in Lagos. Much like my father, he struggled with homesickness, and not the kind you get at a friend's house over the weekend. The music, the malt, the hum of the West African drum, it all felt so familiar, so much like home. Many of my childhood memories, the ones where I watched my dad dance himself drunk, were just that, him soothing his sickness with music and memories.

224

Those dining room dances weren't always exciting. Sometimes, they were sad and soaked with sorrow. The melody of Prince Nico Mbarga's "Sweet Mother" melted into his moans. His eyes ran red with the reality that home was here in North America, now. He wept when he inventoried everything he had left behind, often unsure if it was worth it. Yinka struggled with that same sadness. Unfulfilled by the life he'd found in America, coming to terms with this pyramid scheme called the American dream.

It was different seeing this homesickness as a child. The proximity kept me from the ugly pain of it. Nevertheless, pain is passed between partners, which means I experienced Yinka's unhappiness from under a microscope. A perspective I had never been privy to.

There was always something for West Africans to celebrate, even in Pittsburgh's tiny community. I can recall the nights when my father would return home from an evening of all-night partying—banging at the door for his beloved Dorothy to answer. Many nights, she refused. Patience and I would sneak down the stairs and unlock the door, only to find my father in a spirits-induced slumber. As young girls, we felt sympathy for him. We didn't know he was drunk off his ass. But again, it speaks to the privilege of parenthood, the unearned grace given by children to the people who raise them. We didn't have any help dissecting the situation or understanding why my father's drunkenness was such a disgrace. Our perspectives were padded by what little we knew, which unfortunately, wasn't much.

We often saw my mom frustrated and flustered, worn down, and without rest. Meanwhile, Dad seemed to always be upbeat and in good spirits. Mom had few friends and rarely spent time away from the house. On the other hand, Daddy was the life of the party, hardly ever missing an event. Mom was too busy doing heads full of hair and laying out Sunday dresses to have a social schedule of her own. A Sunday of solitaire was her way of resting, and that's honestly if we let her.

As a child, I didn't have the foresight to see that the kind of partners my parents were to one another played a pivotal role in who they were to me. My dad had space and the energy to contribute more. He chose, instead, to invest that energy elsewhere. My mother was at her capacity, tired, stressed, and alone most nights. Taking on most of the household tasks and bearing most of the burden of parenthood by herself. Sometimes, it seemed marriage made for a lonely life.

It was my mother who accompanied us to doctors' appointments. She was the one who sewed ripped jeans and read over writing assignments. She did all that and more without an outlet; no weekly rendezvous to look forward to. Her days began and ended with her babies; she saw parenting as her most pressing job. That was my mother's routine, day in and day out, with a lot of pleas, little to no praise, and nothing but a sense of obligation to keep her on task.

If she didn't do it, it didn't get done. She was the glue that bound our Monday to Sunday. That is the beauty and the burden of being birthed by a strong Black woman; there's little room for her to be much of anything else. My mother was strong when I needed her to be soft and indifferent when I needed her to be empathetic. She showed up every time, just never quite with the right tools for the job. She was tired of carrying the toolbox, tending to everyone else's needs while having hers ignored. Any human would grow weary of that arrangement.

But good mothers didn't moan about the woes of womanhood, and my mother so desperately wanted to be one of the good ones. Good mothers wrapped their wrath in silence, conserving their cries for spaces where they couldn't be counted. They had to be happy, raise well-behaved children, often, alone. They made home-cooked meals, baked pies for parties, and ran for president of the PTA, doing it all in four-inch pumps.

My mother wanted to be a good mother. She tried to bake bread and pluck fresh vegetables from her garden. She wanted to play a more active role in our lives, to be a part of our plans. But for my mother to be the mother she wanted to be, my father needed to be the partner she needed, a more proactive partner, one who equally engaged in the mundane day-to-day tasks of parenthood. This would have allowed my mother to enjoy not only the non-essential side of parenting but also essential time with herself, practicing self-care, something we now consider crucial to a person's mental and physical well-being.

For the sake of being a good woman, a good wife, a good mother, my mother sacrificed being a good person to herself. Unintentionally, she offered us too. It sounds silly to prioritize others' opinions over the needs of yourself, but that's precisely what society says mothers should practice. Society says mothers should ignore indications from their brains and bodies that they need a break. Society says mothers should muscle through depression and signs of a postpartum disorder, that there is something wrong with a woman who doesn't desire to nurture nonstop. According to the West's way, motherhood is about laboring for leverage and investing in our children to anticipate a payout. My mother believed that because she labored over us, loving us was optional. Not that she had the energy to do both, anyway.

She did what she thought good mothers were supposed to do. Provided us with the necessities and maintained our physical upkeep. She made sure we understood the importance of education, excelled academically, and had a healthy fear of God. She overlooked marital misgivings for the sake of supplying us with a two-parent household. She kept quiet when she was right and spoke softly when presenting a challenge. She did everything society says a woman should do to keep order in the home and make their partner feel important.

She was the quintessential strong Black woman, putting the greater good above her happiness. But we suffered the back blow of having an unhappy mother. We cannot hide unhappiness. In one area of our lives or another, it will rear its ugly head. It looks like irritability, moodiness, and mean-spiritedness, like hopelessness, anxiety, judgment, and pessimism. The beauty and the burden of being birthed by a strong Black woman is that she's typically a tired woman too.

As a child, I thought I wanted to marry a man like my father. It turns out; I didn't know my dad that way. I couldn't assess his performance from a perspective I didn't have. My opinions were packed around his doings as my dad. Not to mention, his demure demeanor stood in staunch contrast to the negative narratives I had been fed about Black fathers. From where I was standing, my dad was a deity. My desire to marry a man like him was more about what I desired for a parenting partner than a husband. A man who doted on his daughters like his life depended on it. There were undeniable things about my father I wanted my husband to emulate. How he treated my mother wasn't one of them. Not that he mistreated her, per se. It's just that he was a partial partner, an additional dependent in many instances. Patriarchy makes men the prize, and the prize is to be kept, not stressed.

The marker for manhood is so low you could trip over it. Yet, we're bombarded with ways to be worthy women. Whether it's maintaining a specific body size or type or adhering to certain social codes, accommodating unwanted social interactions, the guidelines for womanhood are there. We have been binding and squeezing and tying our bodies to mollify the male gaze for centuries. Having babies because society says it's womanly, dragging down the aisle because a good woman becomes a wife.

And we've stayed home and raised the babies, cooked the meals, and kept quiet, endured infidelity after infidelity and affair after affair. Good women understood that good men weren't always good; they didn't fault them for that. They showed grace and forgave freely. They officered other women and always gave men the benefit of benevolence. If you weren't doing all that, could you call yourself a good woman?

Meanwhile, the worst man is just one donation away from decency. It's not uncommon for men to undeservedly be viewed as virtuous, sometimes based on social legacy alone. My father made a commitment to my mother to stay, and that's just what he did, which is still more than many other men can say for themselves. In no way am I dismissing the weight of his dedication. But look at all my mother had to do to be a good woman. Look at everything she had to lose first, all the pieces of herself she had to part with.

My father was a good man based on his public proclamation to stay with the woman he made a mother. That was all it took. I can't count how often I heard how lucky I was that my father married my mother, that he was active in our lives, and that he hadn't run off with some other woman. For my father to be great, the only requirement was that he stay. Everything done in addition to that was considered a bonus.

So, when he made us an after-school snack, we celebrated his culinary skills. When he put our hair up in lopsided puffs, we praised him for his patience. When he bribed us with Burger King to sit quietly through his weekday mass, we toted his multitasking abilities. And when he remembered special dates, we praised his selflessness, no matter how many times he had forgotten in the past.

The cycle was repeating in me. Without genuinely knowing the woman my mother was, I had become a woman just like her. I was angry, embittered, anxious, and temperamental. I was feeling trapped in a relationship that required me to contribute on behalf of both of us. Adeyinka was a good person, but he wasn't a good partner, at least not for me. It took time for me to discover the distinction.

I had idolized my father my entire life, placing him on a pedestal as the pinnacle of what it meant to be a good man; I wasn't wrong about that. He was kind, loving, loyal, and smart. But I was wrong about that being enough. It's not enough to just be a good man. Men must do the work to be good partners too. Adeyinka was good with just being good, and that wasn't good enough for me.

My mother missed an opportunity to be honest with us about marriage, about the importance of choosing a present and supportive partner. We needed open and honest discussions about dating and marriage with her, even if they delved into her disappointment. Often, women who follow the patriarchal path to perfection become disillusioned by the reality of what they find on the other side. They can feel ashamed or swindled. Some may even be unwilling to acknowledge that the prize they won wasn't all that worth it. But it is a truth that young girls need to hear; that marriage isn't validation or a warrant for their worth, nor their character predicated on their ability to occupy a man's attention.

Having more awareness of my mother's struggles with motherhood and marriage wouldn't have made me love my father any less. However, it would have made me far more empathetic to my mother as a person, beyond whatever job description her title tied her to. That is the power in sharing our stories with our children. The wisdom we hold within our lived experiences as women is just what young girls need to navigate a world that would have them on an equally poisonous path to perfection. We empower young girls by gifting them our allegory, by sharing with them our songs, by existing in our truth and doing so right where they can see us. It is an act of oppression not to.

Far too often, mothers are the first people to oppress their daughters, teaching them by example to silence themselves, ignore their needs, and prioritize unsolicited opinions. We teach our daughters to sacrifice their happiness in the hopes of being beneficial. Instead of using our disenfranchisement to develop a sense of awareness within them, we do this instead of instilling a desire to exist beyond someone's interpretation of good. It's common for mothers to start their daughters at a deficit, feeling slighted by their missteps. Subconsciously hoping they're dealt the same defeat. Is it any wonder that misogyny makes women miserable?

That it makes it difficult to wish well on the next woman, even if she is your daughter. We have all known mothers who've marked their daughters as competition. It's not unheard of for women to war with the potential their daughters possess. Misery loves company, and misogyny makes women miserable. And you don't get happy mothers from miserable women.

If you marry a man like your father, you end up a woman like your mother. They may actually be right about that. Between Adeyinka's late-night lifestyle and his affinity for alcohol, I barely slept most nights. I had become a caregiver, a personal assistant, a second mother of sorts. My anxiety was through the roof as Adeyinka enjoyed a delayed adolescence. I was relegated as the adult in the relationship and held to impossibly high standards. He was the prize; I was expected to do whatever necessary to keep him. I had someone who had committed to committing to me. That was more than what most men were willing to do.

As a child, I believed that to be enough. It's all I'd ever been told; womanhood was getting the guy to stay and discovering different duped me. Why hadn't any of the women in the family warned us about womanhood? It was unfulfilling and unfair as far as I could see; they hadn't thought to mention that part? Being with Adeyinka meant being the woman he wanted while waiting on him to become a man worthy of me. It meant working to be a good woman, working to be a good wife, while waiting on him to decide whether he wanted to be a present partner to me. It meant hiding my frustrations and quieting my concerns to preserve my partner's ego.

I learned to bury my bones by watching my mother hide hers. And under similar pressures, I mirrored her practices, proof that our parents' behavior is learned, whether we know it or not. She couldn't teach me what she wasn't practicing. She couldn't protect me from the pain she pretended didn't debilitate her daily. I thought I wanted to marry a man like my father until one day my mother was me.

CHAPTER 13

WOMAN TO WOMEN

A JOURNAL ENTRY ON DOMESTIC VIOLENCE

Did your mother know Carlos was abusive?"

"She did," I admitted to Ms. Lynn. We'd been at this now for fifteen weeks and had built quite the rapport, using my childhood journals as a guideline for growth.

"Did she ever say anything to you about it, encourage you to leave?"

"There was this one time she stopped by unannounced with my older cousin—he hulled around my apartment for a while, inspecting things and just generally being intimidating. Carlos wasn't concerned. Before I knew it, he and my mom were chit-chatting about oldies. He was a charmer, and my mother wasn't hard to charm."

"Did that bother you?"

"Yes, and no. I know my mother. I know she's gonna find a way to take a man's side. When you're in a situation like that, you can't throw up your hands and yell for help. I wish she'd paid it a little more attention. You know? But I guess she didn't know me well enough to see the signs."

"Until that point, had you any idea of your mother's history with domestic violence?"

"No, I had no idea. We all knew her first marriage ended badly, but we never knew the details."

"So, you find out after two years of torture, after almost losing your life, after leaving everything behind and moving to Texas, that your mother was a survivor herself. How does that make you feel?"

"A part of me feels like she was embarrassed. I guess I understand why."

"What about the other part?"

"The other part is just pissed. I feel like they set us up to fail in so many ways; them, being the women in my family. We knew nothing about our bodies, only to hide them and to be ashamed. We knew nothing about boys, about safe dating, about choosing a healthy partner. My parents' thought being married where we could see them was supposed to suffice. And sure, that counts for something, but everyone else was talking to us about life. I learned about sex from a 10-year-old friend for fuck's sake!"

"So, you're saying they could have taught you all more by telling you about their experiences?"

"Well, yeah. Isn't that what parents are supposed to do? If I have a daughter, I am definitely teaching her how to spot a potential abuser. I feel like that's my job. How can I know what I know and not share it with her? It's cruel. My mother's decision was cruel."

"Take me to Dallas, to your old apartment. What's happening the day Carlos comes over?"

"I had just moved into this place. I had no furniture at all, and I mean nothing, not even an air mattress. It was just me and my laptop on the floor, enjoying the sanctity of my solitude. Then there's a knock at the door. I look out through the peephole, and it's this brown-skinned lady asking for me. I crack the door slightly open so that I can see her better. And as soon as I do, the door slams into my face! WAM! Carlos rushes through the door, and my life flashes before my eyes. I knew he was there to kill me."

"But you're not dead." Ms. Lynn smiled at me.

"No, I'm not." I smiled back. "Almost." I laughed.

Ms. Lynn laughed too. "And what do they say about almost? Doesn't even count."

"Right." We laughed again.

On a couple of occasions, I've asked myself what it might've been like to grow up with a mother like Ms. Lynn. Okay, maybe more than a couple. She was so supportive, so honest, and direct with me. I envied her children, who she joked were remarkably unimpressed. Ms. Lynn and I had come a long way in our relationship. I trusted her; she respected me. I was learning the long way that that was all any relationship needed.

"I wanna preface this question I'm about to ask by saying that it's not uncommon for kidnapping victims to have huge gaps as far as their recollection of the incident. It's a natural defense mechanism. The brain attempts to shield you from the effects of the trauma on your psyche. So, I never want you to feel bad if you struggle to recall exactly what happened that day or if the details sometimes seem a little blurry. It's a common thing, and I wanna make sure you understand that."

I nodded to say I understood.

"Now, try to tell me what you recall occurred after Carlos pushed in the door."

"I screamed. The girl at the door did too, who I later learned was his cousin. He started beating me immediately, and I mean wailing on me, like really whipping my ass. His cousin never said a word. She just stood silently in the corner, watching it all unfold. Eventually, I blacked out."

"Was he still there when you came to?"

"He sure was. He was threatening to kick me in the head unless I gave him a good reason not to. He had my phone, and I had no way of escaping. We were in there for hours. The beatings would start and stop. I thought I died a few times, but I just kept waking back up. Then it got dark outside, and the cousin got openly agitated. I couldn't hear exactly what they were discussing, but I could tell that she needed to leave. We'd been in there all day at this point. So that's when things got crazy, escalating from bad to worse."

"We can pause and take a break at any time," Ms. Lynn reminded me.

I nodded in response.

"So, they decided that he had to kill me. He pulls me up off the floor and drags me towards the balcony door. I'm on empty at this point, clawing at the carpet with the little strength I have left, and he's just dragging me like a rag doll towards the sliding door. Now, I'm screaming because I realize he's trying to toss me over the railing! I'm kicking and screaming while he's ripping my hands from the railing. I mean, we're wrestling at this point. He has his pelvis pressed against my back and his knee between my legs. He's pushing and lifting, and I'm gripping this railing with all my might. I hear a voice yelling, 'Hey! Hey!' from below my balcony in the middle of all this melee. It's my neighbor watching it all unfold!"

"She keeps yelling at the top of her lungs, 'Hey! Leave her alone! Leave her alone!' Carlos grabs me by my neck and shoves me back inside. Mind you, my neighbor is still yelling. Now she's yelling for help. He forces me out of my apartment and down the stairs. I have no shoes on. My clothes are ripped and torn. He tries forcing me into his cousin's car, but she wouldn't unlock the door. He's fighting me, banging on the window, and tugging at the handle. It's pure chaos at the car. My neighbor runs out of her house with her house phone in her hand. She's at a distance so I can't hear what she's saying. I am just praying she's calling the cops."

"Eventually, his cousin unlocks the car door, and she is visibly upset. He climbs into the back seat beside me, and they start arguing back and forth. I'm just crying my eyes out at this moment. I'm sure he's going to kill me at this point. I'm thinking it's a matter of where, not if. I'm crying so hard; I start to hyperventilate. He's yelling at me to breathe. I'm grabbing at my chest, and she's yelling at both of us. I'm surprised we didn't just drive right into a ditch. By now, I must have been blue or something because out of nowhere, he tells her to take me to the hospital. We're both confused by that."

"They argue for a minute, and at this point, she is over the whole heist. She drives us to the hospital, which was only about a five-mile drive from my apartment in Irving.

Between my chest getting tighter and tighter and Carlos keeping me hostage, I wasn't sure I would make it. We get there. He hops out, swings open my car door and drags me out onto the concrete. I'm lying there thinking I can't believe he's just about to let me go like that. Thank God! Right? Wrong!"

"He goes back and forth with his cousin for a minute. She peels off, and I am in disbelief. I can only imagine how out of your mind you must be to abuse someone for the better part of the day, try to toss them off a balcony, and then accompany them to the hospital for treatment. I mean, it's almost like he was so set on killing me and had become so focused on finishing what he set out to do that he'd completely lost touch with reality. Here I am hobbling into the hospital in the arms of my abuser. It almost wasn't real."

"Do you have any idea how Carlos caught up with you once you fled Pittsburgh?"

"I had no idea at the time, which made it much scarier. After his arrest, Carlos wrote me a letter to let me know that my mother told him where I was. It was his way of digging in the knife."

"How did that conversation come about?"

"He called her to complain. To tell her I abandoned him at my apartment that he refused to leave, that I never told him I was leaving, that he had no idea why I even left. Essentially, I up and disappeared without reason, and he was sick about it. He told her how I avoided her calls and pretended I wasn't home when she visited. He didn't tell her I was hiding black eyes and wasn't permitted to speak to family without being punished for it. She never even asked me for my side of the story."

"What about his friends, family? Were they aware of the situation? Did anyone advise him otherwise?"

"Carlos was surrounded by enablers. His whole family knew he had rage issues, possibly an alcohol addiction. Even his former teammates were familiar with his temper. There were times he showed how short his fuse was right in the middle of the basketball court. The coaches, staff, everyone covered it up because, well, Carlos was a star. Who could control 'Black Magic'? It was all a part of the alter ego. And when his basketball career didn't pan out, it was too late for anyone to reel him in. My mother buying into his good-guy appeal was no different than anything anyone else had done."

"Have you ever spoken with her about any of this?"

"Nope. It's like it didn't even happen."

"Do you want to talk to her about it?"

"Not particularly. It's not like she would apologize."

"But what if she did?"

"I'd probably just feel bad. Feel like I beat her up about it. As much as I want my mom to know that she's done things to hurt me, I don't want her hurt in return."

"It's natural to feel that way about your mother, even when she has exhibited some abusive behaviors. Some research has been done on attachment and abuse, and one of the most resilient bonds of the burden of abuse is the parent-child bond. You wouldn't be the first person to want to protect your abuser from the pinch of the pain they've caused you. It's a pretty common thing."

We nod in agreement.

"So, the cousin drops the two of you at the hospital, and what happens from there?

"So, he picks me up off the concrete and half carries me into the ER. He drops me in a chair, walks right up to the registration desk and starts having a conversation with the woman waiting there. He points her in my direction, and I do my best to give her the quick crazy eye. Anything to say, 'I am not okay'. I'm doubled over in pain, my chest still tight. He couldn't convince the woman at the counter that this was an urgent enough emergency, so she sends him back with a clipboard, and I proceed to fill the pages. He's not saying anything to me or barely making eye contact, but I can tell it's business as usual. I'm expected to pretend there's nothing going on, play the part so that we can get out of here and finish what he came to do. Real sick shit."

"It is," Ms. Lynn interjects.

"So, eventually, I get called back to triage, and this nurse comes in and starts asking me questions. Carlos is answering them for me. She's looking at me, I'm looking away, Carlos is looking at her, and everyone is talking to the side of someone else's head. Everyone except me; I say nothing because, you know, it's business as usual. So, the nurse is becoming suspicious. I mean, Carlos was off the hinge; he smelled of alcohol, and I had tell-tale signs of physical abuse. She was putting two and two together.

"You think Carlos could feel the walls closing in?" Ms. Lynn asked.

"Oh, he knew, and he was getting steadily agitated. The longer we stayed there, the longer the nurse went back and forth, bringing more people into the room, the more anxious he became. At one point, she steps out of the room, and he accuses me of looking at her funny. And when she returns, he tells her we're just about ready to go. She says they need to do one physical examination before we leave, and she's persistent, as persistent as he is. Another nurse steps into the examination room, and they tell Carlos that he has to step outside. He's not happy about that. He argues with them, listing the ridiculous reasons he needs to be there with me. They go back and forth for a while, and then he tells me to stand up so we can leave. But I'm no idiot, so I don't budge. I know if I leave this hospital with him, I'm dead. These nurses are my only hope. So, he repeats it, "Arah, get up! Let's go!" At this point, a cop appears at the door. I think he was a cop. He could've been an armed guard, but he looked like the Terminator standing in that doorway."

We chuckled.

"Either way, I was happy to see him. He asks Carlos to step outside of the examination room. And he's on ten; eyes bugged, veins bulging, voice raised and everything. He refuses to step outside the room, so the officer steps in. He doesn't touch him; he stands there and talks to him for a while. The nurses are both standing by the door, mouthing things to me. I can only imagine what they were attempting to tell me. Maybe that help was on the way because a few minutes later, two more cops popped up at the door. Once Carlos saw them, he agreed to leave the room. The nurses rush over to me. They're looking me up and down, asking me questions about Carlos. In the background, we can hear him arguing with the cops. They're asking if he caused the bruises to my body, and I'm saying 'No'. I didn't know whether they planned to arrest him or allow him to leave. I was hesitant to give them too many details.

'Are you sure he didn't hit you?'

'Yes, I'm sure.' I continued to lie. Just then, we hear a shuffle coming from the hallway. Carlos and the cops are in an all-out brawl. That pretty much ends the interrogation. He's arrested right there at the hospital. And here I am talking to you."

"Well, I'm sure some other things happened in-between here and there, but we can stick a pin in it for today. We covered a lot of ground. You described some difficult situations, all of which took place in a noticeably short amount of time, compounding and intensifying the trauma. I want to know how you're feeling. I'm not going to lie. I was feeling uneasy listening to you tell your story just now."

"I don't get sad anymore but talking about it makes me feel tired."

"Pretty tiring, right?"

"Yeah."

"Yeah, trauma is tiring. That's how you know it's still affecting your body. The fatigue is your brain's way of letting your body know that it's producing more stress than you can cope with."

"Try telling my mom that. I stress I slept my way through high school, and she swore it was sex fatigue," I said sarcastically. Ms. Lynn scrunched her face. "What?!" We both laughed.

"It's been what, six months since your assault, and you're still slowly peeling back the layers and looking at where the break downs occurred, trying to pinpoint your part. Believe it or not, you too play a part. And let's also consider the role the community plays, both in keeping the abuse going and in inserting itself to see that the abuse is kept quiet. The cycle is much more than just you and Carlos caught in toxicity, it's more than just your mother and her ex-husband being bad for one another. The cycle is you, your partner, your family, his family, your friends, his friends, your religion, your entertainment, your social media feeds, etc. The cycle circles around all of it. You understand what I mean?"

"Yeah, I understand what you mean."

"So, when talking about breaking the cycle, we've got to be delicate in how we look back and judge the people who remain trapped in its tangles. And that's with all forms of trauma. How we break the cycle looks different for everyone, and that's because trauma, even when shared, affects us individually. Breaking the cycle for some people looks like leaving an employer. For others, it looks like disassociating from family or childhood friends. For people like you and I, Arah, people with painful family pathologies, our abuse cycle looks a lot more like a labyrinth. We're looking at interconnecting discs of dysfunction. And if you can imagine, it's a lot more difficult to leave the cycle when you're struggling to locate the exit. That's what compound trauma looks like. Trauma stacked on top of trauma. And sometimes, from the other side, we can forget just how difficult it is to escape."

"You are doing a great deal of work to break cycles in your family, and that work is to be commended. But part of that work is acting as a way out for others, not another reason they stay. And what's one of the main reasons we stay trapped in any abuse cycle?"

"Because we're ashamed for anyone to know."

"Exactly. How much do you think shame and fear factored into your mother's decision to keep her victimization a secret?"

"A lot."

"Yeah, probably a lot. And you know what fear and shame lend themselves to?"

"I'm gonna say secrecy."

"I'm gonna say you're right. And when you think about it, it's unfair, because there are parts of your parents' experience that you automatically inherit. I like to call it our inherited genetic identity."

"Uh oh." I adjusted in my seat.

"'Uh oh', is right. It's as scary as it sounds." We laughed. "Imagine that, inheriting your character, your personality from your parents. What if I told you that, in a way, we do? How else do we explain these so-called "generational curses" if not for the phenomenon of an inherited genetic identity? Quite often, the guy that grows up swearing he'll never be like his father, that sees the pain single parenthood caused his mother and commits to being a man of morality, ends up displaying these same deficits when his character is called into question. He's a pathological liar. He's habitually unfaithful. He might even opt out of parenthood once it gets too tough. Why is that? Isn't Mom's impact ample?

Not necessarily. It's not the opposite sex parent who sets the standard for who we should aspire to be. Instead, they set the standard for how we should aspire to be treated. It is, however, the same sex parent that teaches us how to behave in return. Good or bad, we recreate what we know, even if we only know what we've witnessed. No matter how much we want to be the men and women our parents weren't, we carry the same genetic material that made them who they are. It's not enough to want to be better, it takes work to undo the imprint of their identities. Otherwise, their dysfunction becomes our fate."

"We can't unpack what we don't know we're carrying, and we're all carrying parts of our parents. We empower our daughters when we share with them our stories. It's like being given a treasure map and having all the booby traps marked for you. That's not to say you don't ever get off the path, but you feel a lot more prepared for the journey. You feel like you've got a better understanding of what's along the trail, even if the terrain has changed a bit. Just by overcoming the shame of your secrets, you begin to break that cycle. You empower your daughter in a way that your mother hadn't healed enough to empower you."

"Since you've started coming to see me, I've seen so much of that fear melt away. But when we're no longer afraid, it's easy to forget how crippling that fear can be. You know what it's like to exist free from that fear, after the three decades you've spent in secrecy. Does your mother know that feeling? Do you know how long she's spent in secrecy?"

"I honestly don't know."

Ms. Lynn made me think that session. I'd only ever looked at my mother from the perspective of the maternal metrics she didn't measure up to. But the richness of her womanhood housed the wholeness of who she was. It took two years for me to finally ask my mother the question Ms. Lynn posed to me. Did she know how it felt to be free from fear? She didn't. That fear was the fabric with which her womanhood was weaved. It made sense that she would model our identities around those same insecurities.

It wasn't until I understood my mother as a woman that I could forgive her for who she couldn't be as my mother. And once I had forgiven her for who she wasn't, I could embrace myself for who I had become, recognizing that she was permanently affixed to my adult identity. My mother didn't do her best, but humans rarely do. We're far more inclined to do just enough to squeeze by, to give just enough effort to crawl across the finish line. My mother was strong, but how strong can a Black woman be when she's fighting on all fronts for the right to refuge? Where was her respite? What vessel could she saturate while hers sat consumed?

This isn't to excuse her decisions while in that dark space, but to humanize who she was while there. Empathy saved me and allowed me to see my mother's womanhood apart from its deformities. That understanding didn't change my mother, but it changed me. It freed me from a thirty-year thirst for validation and affirmation. It also freed me from internal ignorance and my refusal to recognize how I had become a bridge linking one generation of trauma to the next. It is through intentional empathy that mothers and daughters reach restoration. The jewel of the journey was in learning to embrace my mother's reincarnation in me, recognizing the infinite possibilities that recreation represented, and deciding to do good with the power my maternal lineage presented. Even more rewarding than discovering my mother's mortality was learning to love my mother in me.

CHAPTER 14

MOTHER BY ANOTHER NAME

A JOURNAL ENTRY ON RESTORATION

I was 22 the first time I met my mother. And by my mother, I mean Dorothy Jean. Don't get me wrong; I was raised by the woman who birthed me, so there's no confusion about the legal name and identity of my mother. I know who my mother is, but I didn't know Dorothy, the woman, that is. The muse behind the mom.

I grew up hearing stories about my mother. How beautifully and boldly she had bloomed throughout the years. She was raised in a full house. Being the eldest daughter of ten children, she quickly carved herself out to be her clan's cornerstone. She was quick-witted and calculated according to my uncles, lively and loving according to her sisters, but everyone agreed on one thing about my mother; Dorothy Jean was not the type to back down from a brawl.

But most of the stories we heard about my mother were muddled, murky, at best: her first marriage, her rumored arrest, the fallout with her congregation of faith. All of it was unspoken, whispered about behind the bustle of family functions. That was how my mother preferred it. She questioned what anyone would do with that information anyway, besides talk about her behind her back, something she believed women often did. My mother was a woman who did not trust other women. After experiencing repeated violations of privacy and trust, not just at the hands of women to whom she shared no relation, but with some to whom she did, she swore never to trust another soul.

The encounters were eye-opening for my mother, downright defeating sometimes, as extreme trauma can often be. After enduring repeated pain episodes, our brains zero in on the source, often becoming hyper-focused on it to avoid it further. My mother had endured her fair share of trauma, and it made her entire

community, including her home, appear unsafe. She felt
if she were never vulnerable, open, and transparent in the
present, no one could ever hurt her with her past. She kept
a safe distance from friends, and to an extent, even my
dad. She kept things just above the surface when it came
to her children. There was just a lot about my mother that
we did not know. That was by design. She thought that
she could be one way with the world, and another way
with her family. But she was wrong. Who we are as
women, we're bound to become as mothers. If our inner
woman is in turmoil, our motherhood will be too.

The day I met my mother started with a visit to my
parents' home. My '92 Camry barely made its way up the
steep Pittsburgh hill that housed my parents' two-story. I
used my door key to let myself in and greeted my sister's
anxious dog upon entering.

"Hi Dad, where's Mom?" I asked, noticing he was
cooking in the kitchen.

"Kedu ka imelu, Arah," he replied. "Momma is
upstairs."

I trotted up towards the room. In between a few soft knocks, I called out to my mom and slowly pushed the bedroom door open.

"Mom?" I called out again, as I noticed her awake but unresponsive.

"Mom, what's wrong?" I asked, frozen in front of her dresser.

I wanted to approach my mother as she sat with her legs folded, rocking side to side on top of her cranberry-colored comforter but decided against it. My instincts told me something had to be wrong and very wrong at that. Dorothy Jean did a lot of things; crying was not one of them.

"Mom," I said again, almost in a whisper. This time my semi-salutation garnered a response. "Hmm?" she moaned, still rocking side to side. My first thought was who died and when was the funeral. When you grow up in a household where explanations are reserved for adults, you learn to rely on your anxiety for answers.

"Mom, what's wrong?"

I was hoping to hurry the hurt along. The only thing worse than growing up in a family full of secrets was always being the last one to know about them. I inched closer to the edge of the bed, now more alarmed than anxious.

"Mom," I repeated. "Mom, what's wrong?"

Her rock now seemed more like a shake.

"I miss my mother," she burst into tears. "I miss Mommy." Tears streamed from her face.

We lost my maternal grandmother some years back. The details of her death, over time, became just another secret for our family to smother. The impact of her influence was no secret at all. My grandmother was as fierce as the fiery red ringlets that shaped her slender face. Her fruit didn't fall far from the tree.

Later in her life, my mother would take on more of a caretaker role, tending to my grandmother's health, housing needs, and seeing her upkeep and safety. Despite her ongoing health challenges, my grandmother was in good spirits the last time I saw her. For some reason, that doesn't deliver as much solace as you would expect.

I chose not to stay with my grandmother the weekend they discovered her body. I had a bunch of bullshit I planned to partake in, instead. Today, I can't recall a single significant thing. As much as I loved a good *Walker Texas Ranger* rerun, we didn't get too many sunny weekends in Pittsburgh, and my sisters and I planned to take full advantage. There was always next weekend, or the weekend after that, at least that's what I told myself. We went about our weekend as though it wouldn't be Grandma's last. Imagine my disbelief when it was.

As my mother told us that the body of our deceased grandmother had been brutalized in the bathroom of her one-bedroom that fateful weekend, I grew sick with guilt and grief. I needed to know what happened to her. My mother was mum on the details once again. I know now it was because she didn't have that many, not that I think she would have shared them if she did. The police refused to open an investigation, despite pleas from my family.

I couldn't help but think had I spent the weekend with my grandmother, that I could've prevented this from happening. That's what I felt at that age. Instead, I chose myself and my middle school mindlessness, something I would regret for the rest of my life. And now I'd lost my grandmother, one of the few women who made me feel both seen and supported. How would I ever get past this pain?

The more tears fell onto the living room floor during my mother's impromptu eulogy, the smaller the room began to feel. My father sat at my mother's right side, embracing her as she spoke. His tears fell freely as he prayed to himself.

"She's at peace," he declared.

"Mother-in-law is at peace."

My mother, who had yet to shed any tears, spoke of the funeral arrangements with a blank expression. She shared travel plans with us and mentioned a list of last-minute items she'd be handling throughout the week, one of which would be gutting Grandma's apartment.

I watched my mother closely as she swayed back and forth, in-between my father's arms. I told myself she was just trying to hold it together, be the stronger of the ten siblings; how could anyone be mad at that? The funeral came and went. We watched as they lowered our beloved matriarch into the mud. Temi, who had spent the most time with Grandma, wailed under the weight of our great loss. Her knees buckled as she struggled for self-control.

My uncles rushed in to cushion her collapse. My mother joined him in helping her to her feet. She looked exhausted, rocking Temi from side to side. I looked on, feeling guilty. I should have been there to help. But I lacked the strength.

My mother didn't cry that day. Not that day, or the next day. Not the day after that day, or the one after that. In fact, for years, my grandmother remained unmourned. I watched my mother rock side to side some six years later; tears crashed into her collarbone. It was the first time I'd seen my mother cry. She was conditioned to be a strong Black woman. Her sense of womanhood had been sutured to her sense of strength. She believed her public and private identities were never to overlap. Dorothy, the person, wanted to grieve the loss of her mother. Dorothy, the parent, didn't know how to be vulnerable in front of her children and not lose their respect. So, instead, she did neither.

Growing up, my mother was unemotional, impassive at times, guarded, and closed off. She took pride in her posture and adopted a "never let 'em see you sweat" approach. But of all her strengths as a mother, she would say her greatest strength was her poise. It was what made her the mother that she was. But the woman I held that day on the edge of my mother's bed wasn't poised at all. She certainly wasn't proper. She was exposed, unwrapped, and unconcerned with the weight of her wailing. She allowed herself to be held and hugged, without the usual "Mhmm. Now, what do you want?" I saw a wounded woman, Dorothy, for the first time in my life. If only she knew how strong she truly was in that moment, by allowing me to be strong in her place.

I never told my sisters about that day. I wanted to savor the sanctity of that moment for myself. From there, my mother and I would go on to share many more. And as I share it today, I want to be clear in my intentions; to impart the importance of seeing ourselves beyond the borders of the roles we occupy, mother being the most restricting of them all. Maternal instincts are hardly instinctual. They're barely even maternal. Motherhood is a seat we're seated in, a role we learn to execute.

In the same way that judges deliver judgment through the perspective of their prejudices, and doctors diagnose patients based on their beliefs and bias, mothers mother through the wits and will of their womanhood. That's right. You'll never be a better mother to someone else than you are a person to yourself.

The most precious parts of my mother were what she mistook for weaknesses. She feared that displaying her deficiencies in front of her children would make her a defective mother. Wrong again. We needed to see her sensitive side to be empathetic towards others, especially other women. We needed to see emotion and passion that weren't rooted in provocation so we could learn to express emotion in a healthy, harmless way. We needed to see my mother cry to know that we had permission to process our feelings, without fear of appearing feeble.

The pressures of muted motherhood set us up for an emotional stoppage. We cannot shed the imperfections of our humanity to achieve a motherhood free of human error. Our flaws, our experiences, our quirks, distinguish us as mothers. The more we attempt to silence ourselves, the more our motherhood suffers. That's because who we are as mothers is intrinsically connected to who we've become as women. We'd likely go mad trying to differentiate between the duo. Sometimes we actually do.

The person I thought was my mother growing up was the embodiment of her shelled soul. She had fallen victim to the violent narrative that convinces women that silence and suffrage are their greatest gifts, and in her psychological solitude, she became embittered, her exterior, brittle. When we feel trapped by the terms of our tenure as mothers, we expel that emotional exhaustion onto our children, knowingly or unknowingly. In letting go of the world's way of defining motherhood, we learn that what makes motherhood so special is the ability to express it in our own way.

Our children need to know us as people, and not just as it pertains to our position in their lives. We've become so bound by the idea that our motherhood is our mask, but truth be told, it's unnatural to muddle human emotions behind mothering. That's asking humans to be inhuman, and no matter how much we want mother to be synonymous with magic, the words are hardly interchangeable.

My mother didn't suddenly become an open book with me following our rugged face to face. But our interaction challenged a nagging narrative of hers, one that says that women are inherently untrustworthy. If you had asked my mother why she hid herself, she would say it was done for our benefit. She'd say she didn't want her daughters idolizing her dysfunction, that telling us about her past would be speaking it into our future. That in shielding us from her humanity, she could save us from the hurt her humanness caused her.

Truthfully, her concern was that we would wield her weaknesses to inflict harm on her like other women in her life. My mother's life experiences, both the good and the bad, had framed her outlook on womankind so much that she saw skepticism as a means of security. Unfortunately, that philosophy would become her maternal mantra. My mother believed that women were inherently out to exploit the fragilities of other women. It was an ugly game of dog eat dog, a ruthless cycle of cattiness we were all caught up in. Exposing your hand to your opponent, come on, everyone knew better than that. You played it cool, kept your cards close, and never let them see you sob.

My mother had been hiding her hand, smothering her sound for so long that she had forgotten the might of her moan. I saw her humanness, and it helped me appreciate the real Dorothy Jean that much more. I have always loved my mother; I just never had the opportunity to enjoy the actual individual that I loved. A woman with a huge heart, a sensitive woman, a righteous woman who loved with her whole heart, and hurt with it too. I loved a wounded woman, a complex woman, a woman who was so much more than just my mother. More than anything else she could show me at that moment, she showed me just what I needed to see. Her.

ABOUT THE AUTHOR

Arah Iloabugichukwu was born and raised in Pittsburgh, Pennsylvania. She's been running from the snow ever since. Imposter syndrome survivor and former self defeatist, she spends her time penning literary pieces on popular culture, social justice issues and human behavior. She lives in Houston, Texas with her loving family.

Made in the USA
Columbia, SC
02 December 2021

50172872R00167